REAL VARIABLE

UNIVERSITY MATHEMATICAL TEXTS

GENERAL EDITORS

ALEXANDER C. AITKEN, D.SC., F.R.S.
DANIEL E. RUTHERFORD, D.SC., DR.MATH.

REAL VARIABLE

JAMES M. HYSLOP

M.A., Ph.D., D.Sc.
PROFESSOR OF MATHEMATICS IN THE UNIVERSITY OF WITWATERSRAND
JOHANNESBURG, SOUTH AFRICA

OLIVER AND BOYD

EDINBURGH AND LONDON

NEW YORK: INTERSCIENCE PUBLISHERS INC.

FIRST PUBLISHED 1960

34825

QA 331.5
H 9

PRINTED IN GREAT BRITAIN
BY OLIVER AND BOYD LTD., EDINBURGH

PREFACE

THIS book is designed to fill a gap in the series of University Mathematical Texts. It includes material which is taken for granted in such Texts as Integration and Infinite Series, and may therefore be regarded as the foundation on which each of these rests. The book ranges over such elementary topics as bounds of sets and of functions, the theory of limits, continuity and differentiation, and the properties of the simple functions of analysis.

The exposition of the theory of limits has been made as simple as possible and brevity in this connection has been sacrificed for the sake of clarity. It is a common experience among University teachers that, without a thorough grasp of the concept of a limit, the student is in no position to follow the logical development of mathematical analysis.

In most books on analysis it is usual to base the discussion of the exponential, logarithmic and circular functions on integrals. There is of course no real objection to such a treatment except on the ground of æsthetics. Since the properties of these functions can be derived elegantly from the ideas of limits, continuity and differentiability, it is perhaps preferable to adopt this method rather than make an appeal to definitions by means of integrals. The sooner the student realises that these functions can be rigorously incorporated into the body of mathematics, the sooner will he manipulate them with confidence.

From the point of view of rigour, the circular functions are more awkward to develop than the others. The technique employed in this book, which is based on upper and lower limits and a smattering of convergence theory, is recommended on the grounds that neither integrals nor the multiplication properties of absolutely convergent series are required.

The book is intended for students at the beginning of their study of analysis, whether they are at the first year or later University level, and the chapters are arranged in such a way as to make it suitable both for the elementary and the more advanced reader.

The latter, for example, may wish to follow up Chapter 3 by reading paragraph 5.1 and Chapter 8 before returning to deal with continuity in Chapter 4.

I am indebted to Dr. D. E. Rutherford, Mr. A. J. Thorpe Davie, Mr. D. A. Preece and Miss Wendy Rutherford for helpful criticisms and comments, and I also record my gratitude to Mrs. Frances Herholdt for her work in typing the original manuscript and in assisting with the correction of the proofs.

J. M. HYSLOP

JOHANNESBURG
April 1960

CONTENTS

viii CONTENTS

CHAPTER I

INTRODUCTION

1.1. Real numbers. This introductory chapter deals with the basis on which the subsequent logical development rests. We shall be concerned throughout with real numbers, and it is essential to state explicitly, at the outset, those properties of real numbers which are to be taken for granted. We shall assume that we know what we mean by saying that two real numbers are equal, that we can define operations of addition and multiplication for real numbers, and that these operations obey the following laws:—

Given any real numbers a and b, these numbers have the **commutative** properties

$$a+b = b+a, \quad ab = ba,$$

and, given any real numbers a, b and c, these have the **associative** properties

$$(a+b)+c = a+(b+c) = b+(a+c),$$
$$(ab)c = a(bc) = b(ac),$$

where the insertion of brackets means that the operation within the brackets is to be carried out before any further operation is performed. The common value of the three sums is taken to be the meaning of the sum $a+b+c$ or $c+b+a$ or $b+a+c$, and the common value of the three products is taken to be the meaning of the product abc, cba, bac, etc. Any three numbers a, b, c have also the **distributive** property

$$a(b+c) = ab+ac.$$

Among the real numbers, there is a number 0 and a number 1 which, for any real number a, have the properties that $a+0 = a$ and $a \cdot 1 = a$. We also assume that, for any real number a, there are real numbers x and y such that $a+x = 0$, $ay = 1$, where, in the second case, $a \neq 0$.

From the list of assumptions given above, it is not difficult to *derive* some well-known properties of real numbers. For example, it may be proved that there cannot be more than one zero or more than one unity, that the relation $a+c = b+c$ implies the relation $a = b$, that $a \cdot 0 = 0$, that the relation $ab = 0$ implies either $a = 0$ or $b = 0$, and that the real numbers x and y of the previous paragraph are unique. If these unique real numbers are denoted by $(-a)$ and by a^{-1}, it may also be shown that the equations

$$a+x = b, \quad ay = b \ (a \neq 0),$$

have respectively unique solutions $b+(-a)$, which is written $b-a$, and $b \cdot a^{-1}$, which is written b/a. We shall not give any proofs of these results here, but simply regard them as our stock-in-trade for the elementary analysis which is developed in the subsequent chapters.

Another important property of the real number system which we assume is that it is ordered. To define what we mean by this term we note that among the real numbers there are **positive** real numbers with the properties that 1 is positive and 0 is not, that, for any real number a, we have either a positive, or $(-a)$ positive, or a zero, and that, for any positive pair of real numbers a and b, $a+b$ and ab are positive. Real numbers which are neither zero nor positive are called **negative**. If, for real numbers, a and b, the number $a-b$ is positive, we say that a is greater than b or b is less than a, and write $a>b$, $b<a$ respectively.

It is now easy to prove that, given two unequal real numbers a and b, either $a>b$ or $a<b$. If $a>b$ it follows that $-a<-b$, and, if a and b are both positive, that

$1/a < 1/b$, while, if c is any other real number, $a+c > b+c$ and, if c is positive, $ac > bc$. Further, if $a < b$ and $b < c$, then $a < c$. The system of real numbers possesses a compactness property. By this statement we mean that, if a and b are any two real numbers with $a < b$, there exists a real number c such that $a < c < b$. If a is not less than b we write $a \geqq b$ or $a \nless b$, and, if a is not greater than b, we write $a \leqq b$ or $a \ngtr b$.

If a is any real number, the real number $|a|$ is defined to be a if $a \geqq 0$ and to be $-a$ if $a < 0$. It follows that $|a|$ cannot be negative. It is called the modulus or absolute value or numerical value of a. Thus $|2| = 2$ and $|-3| = 3$. The inequality $|a| < k$ is equivalent to the two inequalities $-k < a < k$. By inspection of the cases when a and b may be positive, negative or zero, it is easy to see that

$$|ab| = |a||b|,$$

and that, when $b \neq 0$,

$$\left| \frac{a}{b} \right| = \frac{|a|}{|b|}.$$

By a similar method, or by combining the inequalities

$$-|a| \leqq a \leqq |a|, \quad -|b| \leqq b \leqq |b|,$$

we at once obtain the inequality

$$|a+b| \leqq |a| + |b|.$$

Writing a in the form $(a-b)+b$, this inequality gives

$$|a| \leqq |a-b| + |b|,$$

which is the same as

$$|a-b| \geqq |a| - |b|.$$

1.2. Positive integers. Among the real numbers there are numbers which we call the positive integers. The familiar properties of these positive integers may be obtained as consequences of the following postulates:—

(i) the number 1 is a positive integer, and the number 0 is not;

(ii) if n is a positive integer, so also is $n+1$;

(iii) given any positive integer n, no positive integer exists which is greater than n and less than $n+1$;

(iv) any set of the positive integers which contains 1, and which also contains $m+1$ whenever it contains the positive integer m, consists in fact of all the positive integers.

From postulate (ii) it follows that there is no " greatest " positive integer, and postulate (iii) shows that the positive integers do not possess the compactness property mentioned in the previous section. Postulate (iv) leads immediately to the so-called Principle of Mathematical Induction which, in its usual form, may be stated as follows:—

If a property P is known to be true when n has the positive integral value k and if, on the assumption that P is true when n has any positive integral value p, it can be proved to be true when n has the value $p+1$, then the property P is true for every positive integer greater than or equal to k.

As an illustration of this principle, suppose we wish to prove that

$$a(b_1 + b_2 + \ldots + b_n) = ab_1 + ab_2 + \ldots + ab_n,$$

where each symbol represents a real number. From the distributive law this result is true when $n = 2$, that is, for two terms in the second factor. Assuming it to be true when n has the value p, we have for $n = p+1$,

$$\begin{aligned}
a(b_1 + b_2 + \ldots + b_{p+1}) &= a\{(b_1 + b_2 + \ldots + b_p) + b_{p+1}\} \\
&= a(b_1 + b_2 + \ldots + b_p) + ab_{p+1} \\
&= ab_1 + ab_2 + \ldots + ab_p + ab_{p+1}.
\end{aligned}$$

The result is true therefore for $n = p+1$, and therefore for all positive integral values of n greater than or equal to 2.

By using this technique, the commutative and associative laws mentioned in 1.1 may be extended, and shown to hold for any number of terms or factors. The results thus derived form the basis of the elementary algebra of numbers, and rules for the factorisation of expressions, for the solution of equations and for the expansion by the binomial theorem for a positive integral index all follow as easy consequences of them. The results obtained in carrying out such processes will be assumed in the book. The reader will find it instructive to prove the binomial theorem for a positive integral index by using the Principle of Mathematical Induction.

Example: Using the principle of mathematical induction show that $1^2 + 2^2 + \ldots + n^2$, denoted by $\sum\limits_{r=1}^{n} r^2$, is

$$\frac{n(n+1)(2n+1)}{6}.$$

1.3. Rational numbers. The set of all real numbers of the form a/b where a and b are integers, with $b \neq 0$, is called the set of rational numbers. Such numbers satisfy equations of the form $bx = a$, where a and b are integers and $b \neq 0$. With the familiar definitions for addition and multiplication of such numbers, it is easy to see that these operations, together with those of subtraction and division, when applied to rational numbers, will produce rational numbers. Rational numbers may always be taken to have positive denominators. Thus $\dfrac{1}{-2}$ may also be written as $\dfrac{-1}{2}$, if we so desire, and each of these is included in the notation $-\dfrac{1}{2}$. Real numbers which are not rational are

called **irrational,** and the question immediately arises as
to whether there are any irrational numbers.

We may partially answer this question by supposing,
if possible, that there is a rational number $\frac{p}{q}$, say, with
all common factors of p and q removed, for which the
square is equal to 2. On this supposition, $p^2 = 2q^2$,
whence p^2, and therefore p, is an even integer. Writing
$p = 2k$, where k is an integer, we then have $2q^2 = 4k^2$,
whence $q^2 = 2k^2$. Thus q^2, and therefore q, is even, and
we have a contradiction. Hence, if there is a real number
whose square is 2, this number is irrational. The existence
of such a real number is discussed in paragraph 1.4 below.

It will be noted that, in the above argument, we use
the property that any integer may be uniquely expressed
as a product of prime factors.

1.4. Indices. If x is any real number and m is a positive
integer the symbol x^m is defined by the relations

$$x^m = x \cdot x^{m-1}, \quad m = 2, 3, \ldots$$
$$x^1 = x.$$

Thus $x^2 = x \cdot x$, $x^3 = x \cdot x \cdot x, \ldots$, $x^m = x \cdot x \cdot x \ldots \ldots m$
factors. From this definition, we at once deduce the three
Laws of Indices, for positive integral indices, namely :—

I. $x^m \cdot x^n = x^{m+n}$,

II. $(x^m)^n = x^{mn}$,

III. $(xy)^m = x^m y^m$; $\left(\dfrac{x}{y}\right)^m = \dfrac{x^m}{y^m}$,

where x, y are any real numbers and m and n are positive
integers. In the second case of III, y must not be zero,
since neither the left hand side nor the right hand side is
defined in such a case.

If m is a positive integer and x is any real number except
0, the symbol x^{-m} is defined to be $1/x^m$ and x^0 is defined

to be 1; the definition of x^m is thus extended to cases when m may be zero or any integer. With these extended definitions, it will be shown that the laws of indices still hold.

In the case of Law I, if m or n is zero, say $m = 0$, we have $x^m \cdot x^n = 1 \cdot x^n = x^n = x^{n+0} = x^{n+m}$, and if either m or n is negative, say m negative and equal to $-\mu$, we have

$$x^m \cdot x^n = x^{-\mu} \cdot x^n = \frac{x^n}{x^\mu} \begin{cases} = x^{n-\mu} & (n > \mu) \\[2mm] = \dfrac{1}{x^{\mu-n}} & (n < \mu) \\[2mm] = 1 & (n = \mu), \end{cases}$$

and each of these is $x^{n-\mu} = x^{n+m}$. If both m and n are negative, say, $m = -\mu$, $n = -v$, we have

$$x^m \cdot x^n = \frac{1}{x^\mu} \cdot \frac{1}{x^v} = \frac{1}{x^{\mu+v}} = x^{-(\mu+v)} = x^{-\mu-v} = x^{m+n}.$$

In the case of Law II, if $m = 0$, we have
$$(x^m)^n = 1^n = 1 = x^0 = x^{mn},$$
and, if $n = 0$,
$$(x^m)^n = (x^m)^0 = 1 = x^0 = x^{mn}.$$

If m is negative, say $m = -\mu$ and n is positive, we have

$$(x^m)^n = \left(\frac{1}{x^\mu}\right)^n = \frac{1^n}{(x^\mu)^n} = \frac{1}{x^{\mu n}} = x^{-\mu n} = x^{mn},$$

and if m is positive and n is negative, say $n = -v$, we have

$$(x^m)^n = (x^m)^{-v} = \frac{1}{(x^m)^v} = \frac{1}{x^{mv}} = x^{-mv} = x^{mn}.$$

If both m and n are negative, say $m = -\mu$, $n = -v$, we have

$$(x^m)^n = \frac{1}{(x^m)^v} = \frac{1}{\left(\dfrac{1}{x^\mu}\right)^v} = \frac{1}{\dfrac{1}{x^{\mu v}}} = x^{\mu v} = x^{mn}.$$

With regard to Law III, if $m = 0$ we have

$$(xy)^m = (xy)^0 = 1 = x^0 y^0 = x^m y^m,$$

and if m is negative, $m = -\mu$, say, we have

$$(xy)^m = (xy)^{-\mu} = \frac{1}{(xy)^\mu} = \frac{1}{x^\mu}\frac{1}{y^\mu} = x^{-\mu}y^{-\mu} = x^m y^m.$$

Similarly for the second relation in Law III.

To summarise, we may say that the three laws of indices are satisfied for indices which are positive integers, negative integers or zero and for all real numbers for which the symbols concerned have a meaning.

It will be proved later in this book (see Theorem 35) that, if a is any positive real number and n is a positive integer, greater than or equal to 2 there is one and only one positive real number x which satisfies the equation $x^n = a$. This positive real number is denoted by $\sqrt[n]{a}$. If a is zero the symbol $\sqrt[n]{a}$ is to be taken to be zero, but, if a is negative, the symbol $\sqrt[n]{a}$ is to be regarded as being without meaning in the sense that it does not represent a real number. It follows, in particular, that there is one positive real number satisfying the equation $x^2 = 2$, which is denoted by $\sqrt[2]{2}$, or, more usually, by $\sqrt{2}$.

Numbers expressible in the form $\sqrt[n]{a}$ have the following properties (m, n positive integers):—

(i) $\sqrt[n]{a} = \sqrt[mn]{(a^m)}$.

Let $x = \sqrt[n]{a}$; then $x^n = a$, whence $a^m = x^{mn}$ and therefore $x = \sqrt[mn]{(a^m)}$.

(ii) $\sqrt[n]{a}\,\sqrt[n]{b} = \sqrt[n]{(ab)}$.

Let $x = \sqrt[n]{a}$, $y = \sqrt[n]{b}$; then $ab = x^n y^n = (xy)^n$ so that $xy = \sqrt[n]{(ab)}$.

(iii) $(\sqrt[n]{a})^m = \sqrt[n]{(a^m)}$.

Let $x = \sqrt[n]{a}$; then $a = x^n$ and $a^m = (x^m)^n$, whence $x^m = \sqrt[n]{(a^m)}$.

(iv) $\sqrt[m]{(\sqrt[n]{a})} = \sqrt[mn]{a}$.

Let $\sqrt[n]{a} = x$, $\sqrt[m]{x} = y$; then $a = x^n = y^{mn}$ and $y = \sqrt[m]{(\sqrt[n]{a})} = \sqrt[mn]{a}$.

If m is a rational real number of the form p/q where p and q are integers and q is positive, and if x is a positive real number, we define

$$x^m = x^{p/q} = \sqrt[q]{(x^p)},$$

where x^p has the meaning already allotted to it in the case when $p = 0$ or an integer. This definition reduces to the original definition of x^m when m is a positive or negative integer or zero, for, when $q = 1$,

$$x^m = x^{p/1} = x^p.$$

The laws of indices will now be shown to hold for indices of this type.

Suppose that

$$m = \frac{p}{q}, \quad n = \frac{r}{s},$$

where p, q, r, s are integers and q, s are positive. Then, using (i) and (ii), we have, for $x > 0$,

$$\begin{aligned}
x^m \cdot x^n &= \sqrt[q]{(x^p)} \sqrt[s]{(x^r)} \\
&= \sqrt[qs]{(x^{ps})} \sqrt[sq]{(x^{rq})}, \\
&= \sqrt[qs]{(x^{ps+qr})}, \\
&= x^{(ps+qr)/qs} = x^{(p/q)+(r/s)} = x^{m+n};
\end{aligned}$$

also, by (iii) and (iv),

$$\begin{aligned}
(x^m)^n &= \sqrt[s]{\{\sqrt[q]{(x^p)}\}^r} = \sqrt[s]{\{\sqrt[q]{(x^{pr})}\}}, \\
&= \sqrt[sq]{(x^{pr})} \quad = x^{(pr)/(qs)} = x^{mn},
\end{aligned}$$

B

and for $x > 0$, $y > 0$,

$$(xy)^m = (xy)^{p/q} = \sqrt[q]{(xy)^p} = \sqrt[q]{(x^p)}\sqrt[q]{(y^p)},$$
$$= x^{p/q}x^{r/s} = x^m y^m.$$

One further addition to the list of definitions is the following:—

If $x = 0$, we define x^m, for any positive rational real value of m, to be zero. Clearly this minor extension to the definition already given obeys the laws of indices.

The three laws of indices, namely,

$$x^m . x^n = x^{m+n},$$
$$(x^m)^n = x^{mn},$$
$$(xy)^m = x^m y^m,$$

have now been established for rational real indices and for all values of x and y for which the symbols concerned have meanings. They may now be extended by making use of the Principle of Mathematical Induction. The first law in its extended form is

$$x^{m_1}x^{m_2}\dots x^{m_r} = x^{m_1+m_2+\dots+m_r},$$

where m_1, m_2, ..., m_r are rational real numbers, and x is a real number such that each x^{m_r} has a meaning. To prove this, we note that the result is true when $r = 2$. Assume it to be true when $r = p$, that is, we assume

$$x^{m_1}x^{m_2}\dots x^{m_p} = x^{m_1+m_2+\dots+m_p}.$$

Then, when $r = p+1$, we have

$$x^{m_1}x^{m_2}\dots x^{m_p}x^{m_{p+1}} = (x^{m_1+m_2+\dots+m_p})x^{m_{p+1}}$$
$$= x^{(m_1+m_2+\dots+m_p)+m_{p+1}} = x^{m_1+m_2+\dots+m_{p+1}}.$$

Thus the result is true for $r = p+1$. Hence it is true for any value of $r \geq 2$.

The second law may be similarly extended to give

$$\{[(x^{m_1})^{m_2}]^{m_3\dots}\}^{m_r} = x^{m_1 m_2 \dots m_r},$$

and the third to give

$$(x_1 x_2 x_3 ... x_r)^m = x_1^m x_2^m ... x_r^m,$$

subject to the conditions that each side of the relations has a meaning.

Example: If a and b are any real numbers and $a > b$, show that $a^\alpha > b^\alpha$, for any positive rational real number α.

1.5. Summary. The results which have been stated, or in a few cases, obtained by proof in this chapter are now to be assumed. They will be used frequently in what follows. It is especially important to distinguish between symbols which have been defined and those which have not. Examples of the former are

$$2^{-\frac{3}{4}}, \ 0^{\frac{1}{2}}, \ 3^0, \ \frac{0}{5},$$

and of the latter are

$$0^{-2}, \ \frac{5}{0}, \ 2^{\sqrt{2}}, \ (-1)^{\frac{1}{3}}, \ (-2)^{\frac{1}{2}}.$$

It must be remembered that those which are undefined are not subject to any rules of manipulation. Manipulation can only be carried out with symbols which have meaning.

Before we proceed to a rigorous development of mathematical analysis we require one further postulate, and this will be stated at the beginning of the next chapter.

CHAPTER II

BOUNDS OF SETS AND OF FUNCTIONS

2.1. Bounded sets. A collection or aggregate or set of numbers is said to be **bounded above** if there is a number greater than all the numbers in the set, and **bounded below** if there is a number smaller than all the numbers in the set. The set of numbers $\frac{1}{x}$, where $1 \leqq x < 2$, all lie between $\frac{1}{2}$ and 1, the latter included, so that this set is bounded above and below, there being numbers greater than and numbers smaller than all the numbers in the set. On the other hand, the set of numbers $\frac{1}{x}$ where $0 < x < 1$ is not bounded above since, given any positive number K, however large, there are members of the set which exceed K, namely those numbers for which $0 < x < \frac{1}{K}$. This set is bounded below since no number in the set falls below 1. If a set is bounded above and bounded below it is said to be **bounded**.

2.2. Upper and lower bounds. If a set of numbers is bounded above, any number above which no number in the set rises is called an **upper bound** of the set, and any number below which no number in the set falls is called a **lower bound** of the set. For example, in the first of the sets considered in 2.1, all numbers less than or equal to $\frac{1}{2}$ are lower bounds. In the case of the second set, there is no upper bound and all numbers less than or equal to 1 are lower bounds.

We now make one further postulate about the system
of real numbers. Briefly, this postulate states that the
system of real numbers is **complete**, and it is equivalent to
the statement which follows. *If a set of numbers is bounded
above there is a least number above which the numbers of
the set do not rise, and, if a set is bounded below there is a
greatest number below which the numbers of the set do not
fall.* In other words, if a set is bounded above, there is
a **least upper bound** and, if a set is bounded below, there
is a **greatest lower bound**. If E denotes a bounded set of
numbers, we shall denote the least upper bound of E by
$\overline{\text{Bd}}\, E$ and the greatest lower bound by $\underline{\text{Bd}}\, E$.

If E_1 is the first set considered in 2.1, we have

$$\overline{\text{Bd}}\, E_1 = 1, \quad \underline{\text{Bd}}\, E_1 = \tfrac{1}{2},$$

and, if E_2 is the second set, $\underline{\text{Bd}}\, E_2 = 1$. In this latter case
there is no upper bound, and therefore no least upper
bound, but for convenience we sometimes write $\overline{\text{Bd}}\, E_2 = +\infty$.
It is to be clearly understood that the meaning of this last
relation is simply that the set E_2 has no upper bound.
Similarly, for any set E, the relation $\underline{\text{Bd}}\, E = -\infty$, means
that the set E has no lower bound.

It cannot be too strongly emphasised at this stage that
the symbols $+\infty$ and $-\infty$, whenever they occur, have to
be given meanings. They have none apart from definition.

It will be noted, from the examples discussed, that
$\overline{\text{Bd}}\, E$, $\underline{\text{Bd}}\, E$ may be members of E, but need not be. With
the notation already used, we have, for example, $\overline{\text{Bd}}\, E_1$
is a member of E_1, but $\underline{\text{Bd}}\, E_1$ is not a member of E_1. Also
$\underline{\text{Bd}}\, E_2$ is not a member of E_2.

If E is any set of numbers which is bounded above and
if $\overline{\text{Bd}}\, E = M$ then, from the definition of M, we have

(i) Every number in E is less than or equal to M,

(ii) Given any positive number ε,† however small, there
is a member of E which is greater than $M-\varepsilon$.

† Throughout the book ε will denote a positive number, and it is
convenient to think of it as small.

If E is any set of numbers which is bounded below and if $\underline{\mathrm{Bd}}\ E = m$ then, from the definition of m, we have

(i) Every number in E is greater than or equal to m,
(ii) Given any positive number ε, there is a member of E which is less than $m+\varepsilon$.

As an illustration, let E be the set of the positive integers. Then E is not bounded above for, if it were, it would possess a least upper bound M, say. Choose any ε satisfying the inequalities $0 < \varepsilon < 1$. Then there is a member of E, that is, a positive integer N, say, such that $M-\varepsilon < N \leqq M$. From this it is clear that the positive integer $N+1$ exceeds M, thus providing a contradiction.

From this result we deduce immediately that, given any positive real number ε, there is a rational real number r such that $0 < r \leqq \varepsilon$. This follows since there is a positive integer n greater than $1/\varepsilon$, and $1/n$ then satisfies the requirements of the rational number r.

2.3. Properties of least upper and greatest lower bounds.
We now prove some fundamental theorems.

THEOREM 1. *If E is any bounded set of numbers and E' consists of the numbers in E, but with their signs reversed, then*

$$\overline{\mathrm{Bd}}\ E = -\underline{\mathrm{Bd}}\ E', \quad \underline{\mathrm{Bd}}\ E = -\overline{\mathrm{Bd}}\ E'.$$

Let $\overline{\mathrm{Bd}}\ E = M$. Then, for every number x in E, we have $x \leqq M$ and, given any positive number ε, there is a number x_1 in E such that $x_1 > M-\varepsilon$. It follows that every number x' in E' is such that $x' \geqq -M$, and that there is a number x_1' in E', namely $-x_1$, such that $x_1' < -M+\varepsilon$. Since ε is any positive number, it follows that

$$\underline{\mathrm{Bd}}\ E' = -M = -\overline{\mathrm{Bd}}\ E.$$

The second result follows from the first on interchanging E and E'.

If E is not bounded above then given any positive number X there is a member of E greater than X and therefore a member of E' less than $-X$. Hence E' is not bounded below. The relations of Theorem 1 therefore remain true in the cases when $\overline{\mathrm{Bd}}\ E = \infty$, $\underline{\mathrm{Bd}}\ E = -\infty$, provided we interpret $-(-\infty)$ to be $+\infty$.

THEOREM 2. *If E is any bounded set of numbers and E' consists of the members of E each multiplied by a positive number c then*

$$\overline{\mathrm{Bd}}\ E' = c\ \overline{\mathrm{Bd}}\ E, \quad \underline{\mathrm{Bd}}\ E' = c\ \underline{\mathrm{Bd}}\ E.$$

Let $M = \overline{\mathrm{Bd}}\ E$. Then, for every number x in E, we have $x \leqq M$ and, given any positive ε, there is a number x_1 of E such that

$$x_1 > M - \frac{\varepsilon}{c}.$$

Hence, for every number x' in E', we have $x' \leqq cM$ and there is a number x_1' of E', namely cx_1, such that $x_1' > cM - \varepsilon$. Hence $\overline{\mathrm{Bd}}\ E' = cM = c\ \overline{\mathrm{Bd}}\ E$. A similar proof holds for lower bounds.

If E is not bounded above neither is E', and if E is not bounded below neither is E', so that the relations of Theorem 2 hold in the case when E is not bounded provided we interpret $c \cdot \infty$ to be ∞, for c positive.

2.4. Functions. If, to each number x in a set E, there corresponds one number y, then y is called a **function** of x **defined for values of x in E** or, more simply, **defined in E**. For example, if the set E consists of all those numbers x lying between 0 and 2, and if the number y corresponding to each such x is the square of x, then the set of numbers y consists of all numbers lying between 0 and 4. The relation between x and y may be expressed in the form $y = x^2$.

$(0 < x < 2)$.   Other examples are

$$y = \frac{1}{\sqrt{x}}, \; (x > 0),$$

$$y = x^3 + 1, \text{ (all values of } x),$$

$$y = \frac{1}{n}, \; (n = 1, 2, \ldots).$$

In the first of these, the set of numbers y is the set of all positive numbers, in the second, it is the set of all numbers, and, in the third, it is the set of all positive fractions with numerator 1.

Generally, we denote a function of x by symbols such as $f(x)$, $g(x)$, $F(x)$, etc.   The relation

$$y = f(x), \; (a \leq x \leq b),$$

means that y is a function of x defined for all values of x in the **interval** $a \leq x \leq b$.   The set of values of the function $f(x)$ is the set of numbers y which correspond to the values of x in $a \leq x \leq b$.

An interval is said to be **closed** if the end-points are included.   Thus the set of numbers x for which $a \leq x \leq b$ is said to be a closed interval.   An interval is said to be **open** if the end-points are not included.   Thus the set of numbers x for which $a < x < b$ is said to form an *open* interval.

Instead of speaking of the set of numbers x for which $a \leq x \leq b$ we often use a geometrical form of language and speak of the **set of points** x in the interval $[a, b]$ and refer to x itself as a point in or a point of $[a, b]$.   If the interval is open, say $a < x < b$, we denote it by (a, b).

As a rule, we shall be concerned with functions which are defined in open or closed intervals, or for all values of x, or for positive values of x, or for all positive integral values of x.   In the last-mentioned case the symbol x is invariably replaced by the symbol n.   Thus the function

$y = n^2$, without any indication of the set of numbers in which n lies, is assumed to be defined for the positive integers $n = 1, 2, \ldots$. Functions of the positive integral variable n are usually denoted by symbols such as f_n, g_n.

The method of illustrating pictorially the variation of functions by the use of graphs is well-known to the reader, and will not be discussed here. It should, however, be pointed out that functions are not necessarily capable of being graphed. For example, if

$$f(x) \begin{cases} = 1, & (x \text{ any rational number}), \\ = 0, & (x \text{ any irrational number}), \end{cases}$$

then $f(x)$ is defined for all values of x, but its graph cannot be sketched.

Suppose that a function $f(x)$, or $y = f(x)$, is defined in some set of points E. Then all the values of the function, namely all the numbers y corresponding to the various numbers x in the set E, form a second set E', say. If this set E' is bounded above, we say that the function $f(x)$ is **bounded above** in E. If the set E' is bounded below, we say that the function $f(x)$ is **bounded below** in E. If E' is bounded above and below, we say that $f(x)$ is **bounded** in E.

If E' is bounded it possesses a least upper bound and a greatest lower bound. These are denoted by

$$\overline{\mathrm{Bd}}_{E} f(x), \quad \underline{\mathrm{Bd}}_{E} f(x),$$

and are called the least upper bound and the greatest lower bound of $f(x)$ in E. If E' is not bounded above we sometimes write

$$\overline{\mathrm{Bd}}_{E} f(x) = +\infty,$$

and if E' is not bounded below we sometimes write

$$\underline{\mathrm{Bd}}_{E} f(x) = -\infty.$$

Thus

$$\overline{\mathrm{Bd}}_{1 \leq x \leq 2} \frac{1}{x} = 1, \qquad \underline{\mathrm{Bd}}_{1 \leq x \leq 2} \frac{1}{x} = \frac{1}{2},$$

$$\overline{\mathrm{Bd}}_{0 < x < 1} \frac{1}{x} = +\infty, \qquad \underline{\mathrm{Bd}}_{0 < x < 1} \frac{1}{x} = 1.$$

If there is no possibility of ambiguity regarding the set E in which the function is defined, we sometimes omit the E from the symbols

$$\overline{\mathrm{Bd}}_{E} f(x) \text{ and } \underline{\mathrm{Bd}}_{E} f(x),$$

and write simply $\overline{\mathrm{Bd}} f(x)$ and $\underline{\mathrm{Bd}} f(x)$.

We now have the following theorems.

THEOREM 3.   *If $f(x)$ is bounded in E, then*

$$\overline{\mathrm{Bd}} f(x) = -\underline{\mathrm{Bd}}\{-f(x)\}; \quad \underline{\mathrm{Bd}} f(x) = -\overline{\mathrm{Bd}}\{-f(x)\}.$$

Let E' be the set of values of $f(x)$ for points x in E and let E'' be the set of values of $-f(x)$. The numbers in E'' are simply the numbers in E' with their signs reversed. Hence, by Theorem 1,

$$\overline{\mathrm{Bd}}\ E' = -\underline{\mathrm{Bd}}\ E''; \quad \underline{\mathrm{Bd}}\ E' = -\overline{\mathrm{Bd}}\ E''$$

and these, on altering the notation, are the results required.

THEOREM 4.   *If $f(x)$ is bounded in E, and c is some positive number, then*

$$\overline{\mathrm{Bd}}\{c f(x)\} = c \overline{\mathrm{Bd}} f(x); \quad \underline{\mathrm{Bd}}\{c f(x)\} = c \underline{\mathrm{Bd}} f(x).$$

Let E' be the set of values of $f(x)$ for x in E, and E'' the set of values of $c f(x)$ for x in E. Then E'' consists of the numbers of E' each multiplied by a positive constant c. Hence, by Theorem 2,

$$\overline{\mathrm{Bd}}\ E'' = c \overline{\mathrm{Bd}}\ E', \quad \underline{\mathrm{Bd}}\ E'' = c \underline{\mathrm{Bd}}\ E',$$

and the results follow on altering the notation.

THEOREM 5.   *If $f(x)$ and $g(x)$ are bounded in a set E, so also is $f(x)+g(x)$, and*

(i) $\overline{\mathrm{Bd}}\{f(x)+g(x)\} \leqq \overline{\mathrm{Bd}}\,f(x) + \overline{\mathrm{Bd}}\,g(x)$,

(ii) $\underline{\mathrm{Bd}}\{f(x)+g(x)\} \geqq \underline{\mathrm{Bd}}\,f(x) + \underline{\mathrm{Bd}}\,g(x)$.

(i) Let E', E'', E''' denote respectively the sets of values of $f(x)$, $g(x)$ and $f(x)+g(x)$ for values of x in E. We have to show firstly that E''' is bounded and that

$$\overline{\mathrm{Bd}}\,E''' \leqq \overline{\mathrm{Bd}}\,E' + \overline{\mathrm{Bd}}\,E''.$$

Let x be any point in E and let y', y'' denote the corresponding points in E' and E''. Let M', M'' denote respectively $\overline{\mathrm{Bd}}\,E'$, $\overline{\mathrm{Bd}}\,E''$. Then $y' \leqq M'$, $y'' \leqq M''$, so that

$$y' + y'' \leqq M' + M''.$$

Now $y'+y''$ is a point of E'''. Denoting it by y''' we see that, for any y''' in E''',

$$y''' \leqq M' + M''.$$

Hence E''' is bounded above. Let $\overline{\mathrm{Bd}}\,E''' = M'''$. Then $M''' \leqq M' + M''$, for suppose the contrary, namely that $M''' > M' + M''$. Choose any positive number ε such that $\varepsilon < M''' - (M' + M'')$. Then, since M''' is $\overline{\mathrm{Bd}}\,E'''$, there is a point z''' of E''' such that $z''' > M''' - \varepsilon$, and there are then points z', z'' of E' and E'', respectively, such that

$$z' + z'' > M''' - \varepsilon > M' + M'',$$

which contradicts the fact that $z' \leqq M'$, $z'' \leqq M''$.

(ii) In this case $-f(x)$, $-g(x)$ are bounded above and therefore so also is $-f(x) + \{-g(x)\}$. Also, by the first part,

$$\overline{\mathrm{Bd}}\{-f(x)-g(x)\} \leqq \overline{\mathrm{Bd}}\{-f(x)\} + \overline{\mathrm{Bd}}\{-g(x)\},$$

so that by Theorem 3,

$$\underline{\mathrm{Bd}}\{f(x)+g(x)\} \geqq \underline{\mathrm{Bd}}\,f(x) + \underline{\mathrm{Bd}}\,g(x).$$

THEOREM 6. *If $f(x)$ and $g(x)$ are bounded in a set E, so also is $f(x) - g(x)$, and*

(i) $\overline{\mathrm{Bd}}\{f(x) - g(x)\} \leqq \overline{\mathrm{Bd}}\, f(x) - \underline{\mathrm{Bd}}\, g(x)$,

(ii) $\underline{\mathrm{Bd}}\{f(x) - g(x)\} \geqq \underline{\mathrm{Bd}}\, f(x) - \overline{\mathrm{Bd}}\, g(x)$.

Since $f(x)$ and $g(x)$ are bounded in E, so also is $f(x) + \{-g(x)\}$, and it follows by Theorems 3 and 5 that

$$\overline{\mathrm{Bd}}\{f(x) - g(x)\} = \overline{\mathrm{Bd}}\{f(x) + [-g(x)]\} \leqq \overline{\mathrm{Bd}}\, f(x) + \overline{\mathrm{Bd}}\{-g(x)\}$$
$$= \overline{\mathrm{Bd}}\, f(x) - \underline{\mathrm{Bd}}\, g(x),$$

and similarly for the second relation.

In this chapter the symbol ∞ for infinity has appeared on several occasions, and attention has been drawn to the fact that the meaning attached to the use of this symbol must always be clearly defined. It is often convenient to regard the appearance of the symbol as providing a kind of mathematical shorthand. Thus, to interpret $-(-\infty)$ as ∞ enables us, in Theorem 1, to have a single enunciation to include both the bounded and unbounded cases of the set E and, to interpret $c\infty$ as ∞, when c is positive, has the same effect in Theorem 2. It is essential to note that ∞ is *not* a number. A mental picture of infinity as being what may be paradoxically described as " something large ", does no harm, if it is realised that argument cannot be constructed on the basis of such a mental picture as a premise. Argument can only flow from the definition of infinity in each case. Whenever the symbol ∞ is defined in analysis it will often be found useful to interpret symbols such as $-(-\infty)$, $c\infty$, $\infty + \infty$, $\infty \,.\, \infty$ to mean ∞, but the interpretation should be checked in each case. The interpretations themselves arise, of course, from the concept of " something large ".

The theorems proved in this chapter are not essential to the theory developed in the immediately following chapters, but they will be required in Chapter 8, when we discuss upper and lower limits. It may be thought desirable to pursue the topic of upper and lower bounds to its logical successor of upper and lower limits and construct the theory of limits on this basis. Readers who wish to do so may now read parts of Chapter 8 and, after the definition of upper and lower limits, define a limit to be the value of these when they are equal. The derivation of the properties of limits will then follow without great difficulty. Those who prefer a less sophisticated approach to the subject of limits should continue with Chapter 3.

Examples II

(1) Determine

$$\overline{\text{Bd}}_{0 \leq x \leq 2} (2x^2 - 4x + 7), \qquad \underline{\text{Bd}}_{0 \leq x \leq 2} (2x^2 - 4x + 7),$$

$$\overline{\text{Bd}}_{0 \leq x \leq 3} (-x^2 + 4x - 1), \qquad \underline{\text{Bd}}_{0 \leq x \leq 3} (-x^2 + 4x - 1).$$

(2) If $f_n = n$, $\qquad g_n = \dfrac{-n^2}{n+1}$,

find the least upper and greatest lower bounds of $f_n + g_n$, for $n = 1, 2, \ldots$. Compare with Theorem 5.

(3) Find the least upper and greatest lower bounds for $n = 1, 2, 3, \ldots$ of

(i) $\dfrac{(-1)^n n}{2n+1}$; $\qquad$ (iii) $(-1)^n n$;

(ii) $\dfrac{(-1)^n (n+1)}{2n+1}$; $\qquad$ (iv) $1 + \dfrac{(-1)^n}{n}$.

(4) If $f(x) = x^2 + 1$, $g(x) = 2 - x$, for $0 \leq x \leq 1$, show that, for such values of x,

$$\overline{\text{Bd}}\{f(x) + g(x)\} < \overline{\text{Bd}} f(x) + \overline{\text{Bd}} g(x),$$
$$\underline{\text{Bd}}\{f(x) + g(x)\} > \underline{\text{Bd}} f(x) + \underline{\text{Bd}} g(x).$$

CHAPTER III

LIMITS

3.1. Limits as x tends to infinity. Limits of functions of x, or of n, as x or n tends to infinity will first be discussed. It is supposed that the functions concerned are defined for all values of x greater than some number A or, in the case of the positive integral variable n, for all positive integers greater than A. To begin with, we have some formal definitions.

DEFINITION. *A function $f(x)$ is said to tend to infinity as x tends to infinity if, given any positive number K we can find another positive number X, such that $f(x) > K$ for all values of $x > X$.*

A function f_n is said to tend to infinity as n tends to infinity if, given any positive number K, we can find another positive number X, such that $f_n > K$ for all positive integral values of $n > X$.

In these circumstances we write

$$\lim_{x \to \infty} f(x) = \infty, \quad \lim_{n \to \infty} f_n = \infty,$$

or $f(x) \to \infty$ as $x \to \infty$, $f_n \to \infty$ as $n \to \infty$.

These definitions are precise statements of the idea that $f(x)$ or f_n may be made as large as we please by taking x or n sufficiently large. They also provide precise meanings for the symbol ∞ as used in this context. The definitions may be modified by restricting K to be any positive number greater than some fixed positive number.

When such a restriction is imposed on K, without altering the definition in other respects, we still say that $f(x)$ or $f_n \to \infty$ as x or $n \to \infty$.

Example 1. If α is any positive rational real number then $x^\alpha \to \infty$ as $x \to \infty$.

Suppose that $\alpha = p/q$ where p, q are positive integers. Then x^α is defined for all positive values of x. *Choose K* to be any positive number. Then the inequality $x^\alpha > K$ is the same as $x^p > K^q$, which, in turn, is the same as $x > K^{q/p}$. Thus, with the X of the definition equal to $K^{q/p}$, we have $x^\alpha > K$ for all values of $x > X$, and therefore $x^\alpha \to \infty$ as $x \to \infty$. It will be noted that the value of X, which is *calculated*, depends on the value of K which is *chosen*. The argument also shows that, if α is any positive rational number, then $n^\alpha \to \infty$ as $n \to \infty$.

DEFINITION. *A function $f(x)$ is said to tend to minus infinity as x tends to infinity if, given any negative number $-K$, we can find a positive number X, such that $f(x) < -K$ for all values of $x > X$.*

A similar definition applies in the case of the positive integral variable.

The concept, of which this is the precise mathematical statement, is that $f(x)$ may be made as small algebraically as we please by taking x large enough. The symbolic representation of the above is

$$\lim_{x \to \infty} f(x) = -\infty, \text{ or } f(x) \to -\infty \text{ as } x \to \infty,$$

and its analogue for the positive integral variable is

$$\lim_{n \to \infty} f_n = -\infty, \text{ or } f_n \to -\infty \text{ as } n \to \infty.$$

As in the case of the first definition, the negative number $-K$ may be any number less than some fixed negative number.

It is clear from these definitions that, if $f(x) \to -\infty$ as $x \to \infty$, then $-f(x) \to \infty$ as $x \to \infty$, and conversely. For, given any positive number K, we can find a positive number X, such that $f(x) < -K$ whenever $x > X$, and this is the same as saying that $-f(x) > K$ whenever $x > X$.

Example 2. If α is any positive rational real number then $-x^{\alpha} \to -\infty$ as $x \to \infty$.

This follows immediately from Example 1.

DEFINITION. *A function $f(x)$ is said to tend to the limit l as x tends to infinity if, given any positive number ε, we can find a positive number X, such that $|f(x) - l| < \varepsilon$ for all values of $x > X$.*

A similar definition applies in the case of the positive integral variable.

The concept, of which this is the precise mathematical statement, is that $f(x)$ may be made to differ from l by as little as we please by taking x sufficiently large. Symbolically we write

$$\lim_{x \to \infty} f(x) = l \text{ or } f(x) \to l \text{ as } x \to \infty,$$

and, in the case of the positive integral variable,

$$\lim f_n = l \text{ or } f_n \to l \text{ as } n \to \infty.$$

The definition may be modified by supposing that ε is any positive number less than some fixed positive number.

Example.

$$\lim_{n \to \infty} \left\{ 1 + \frac{(-1)^n}{n} \right\} = 1.$$

In this case

$$f_n = 1 + \frac{(-1)^n}{n}$$

is defined for all positive integral values of n. Choose any positive number ε. Then

$$|f_n - 1| = \left| \frac{(-1)^n}{n} \right| = \frac{1}{n} < \varepsilon,$$

for all positive integral values of $n > \frac{1}{\varepsilon}$. Hence, with the X of the third definition equal to $\frac{1}{\varepsilon}$, we have $|f_n - 1| < \varepsilon$ for all positive integral values of $n > \frac{1}{\varepsilon}$. The result follows. It will be noted that the value of X which is *calculated* depends on the value of the ε *chosen*.

3.2. Some theorems on limits when $x \to \infty$. Before proceeding to the proof of theorems based on the definitions which have been given in paragraph 3.1, there are some points which require to be emphasised. In the first place, it is easy to see that if $f(x)$ tends to infinity, to minus infinity or to l as $x \to \infty$, then $f(n)$ tends to infinity, to minus infinity or to l as $n \to \infty$. Suppose, for example, that $f(x) \to l$ as $x \to \infty$. Then, given any positive number ε, we can find a positive number X such that $|f(x) - l| < \varepsilon$ for *all* values of $x > X$. In particular, we must have $|f(n) - l| < \varepsilon$ for *all* positive integral values of $n > X$. The cases when $f(x)$ tends to infinity or minus infinity may be dealt with in the same way. The converse of this result is not true. To see this, it is sufficient to take the example

$$f(x) = 1, \ (x \text{ any positive integer}),$$
$$= 0, \ (x \text{ other than a positive integer}).$$

Since $f(n) = 1$ for all positive integers n, it follows at once from definition that $f(n) \to 1$ as $n \to \infty$. On the other hand, there is no number l which, when a positive ε is given, will make $|f(x) - l| < \varepsilon$ for *all* values of x greater than some number X. There are in fact values of x as large

c

as we please for which $f(x) = 1$, and other values of x as large as we please for which $f(x) = 0$.

This example also shows that, given any function $f(x)$, defined for all values of x or for all values of x greater than some fixed number A, it does not follow that $f(x)$ has a limit when x tends to infinity. The first of the theorems below shows, however, that, if $f(x)$ has a limit when $x \to \infty$, then that limit is the only one. The same remark applies to the case of the positive integral variable.

The theorems proved below, although stated in each case for the variable x, also hold for the positive integral variable n. It is supposed throughout, although this may also on occasion be stated explicitly, that the functions concerned are defined for all values of x greater than some fixed number A.

THEOREM 7. *A function $f(x)$ cannot tend to more than one limit as $x \to \infty$.*

It is clear that $f(x)$ cannot tend both to infinity and to minus infinity, since the inequality $f(x) > K$ for all sufficiently large values of x is incompatible with the inequality $f(x) < -K$ for all sufficiently large values of x.

Suppose now that $f(x)$ is known to tend to a limit l. Then, given any positive number ε we can find a positive number X_1, such that for all values of $x > X_1$ we have $|f(x) - l| < \varepsilon$. This last inequality may be written $-\varepsilon < f(x) - l < \varepsilon$ or $l - \varepsilon < f(x) < l + \varepsilon$. The function $f(x)$ cannot at the same time tend to infinity since, if it did, given any positive number $K(> l + \varepsilon)$, we could find a positive number X_2 such that, for all values of $x > X_2$,

$$f(x) > K > l + \varepsilon.$$

Hence, for all values of x greater than *both* X_1 and X_2, we have the incompatible inequalities

$$f(x) < l + \varepsilon \quad \text{and} \quad f(x) > l + \varepsilon.$$

Similarly $f(x)$ cannot tend both to l and to $-\infty$.

Now suppose if possible that $f(x)$, besides tending to l, may also tend to l', and suppose that $l < l'$. Then, with the ε chosen above, we can find a positive number X_3 such that, for all values of $x > X_3$,

$$l' - \varepsilon < f(x) < l' + \varepsilon$$

Thus, for all values of x greater than *both* X_1 and X_3, we have

$$l + \varepsilon > f(x) > l' - \varepsilon.$$

It follows that $l > l' - 2\varepsilon$, and since this holds for *any* positive ε, we must have $l \geqq l'$, which contradicts the assumption that $l < l'$. Similarly we may derive a contradiction from the supposition that $l > l'$.

The theorem is therefore proved.

THEOREM 8. *If $f(x) = k$ for all values of $x > A$, where k and A are fixed numbers, then $f(x) \to k$ as $x \to \infty$.*

Given any positive ε, we have

$$|f(x) - k| = 0 < \varepsilon,$$

for all values of $x > A$. Hence the result follows from the definition.

THEOREM 9. *If c is a fixed number and if $f(x)$ tends to l as $x \to \infty$ then $c\,f(x)$ tends to cl. If $f(x)$ tends to infinity, so also does $c\,f(x)$, when c is a fixed positive number.*

Suppose that $c \neq 0$. Then, given any positive ε, we can find a positive number X such that, for all values of $x > X$,

$$\left| f(x) - l \right| < \frac{\varepsilon}{|c|}.$$

Hence, for all such values of x,

$$\left| cf(x) - cl \right| = \left| c \right| \left| f(x) - l \right| < \left| c \right| \cdot \frac{\varepsilon}{|c|} = \varepsilon,$$

and therefore $c\,f(x) \to c\,l$ as $x \to \infty$. If $c = 0$, then $c\,f(x)$ is zero for all values of x and therefore, by Theorem 8, tends to zero, that is, $c\,l$, as $x \to \infty$.

In the infinite case, supposing that c is positive, given any positive number K, we can find a positive number X such that for all values of $x > X$, we have $f(x) > K/c$. Hence, for such values of x, we have $c\,f(x) > K$, so that $c\,f(x) \to \infty$ as $x \to \infty$.

Example 3. If α is any positive rational number, $a\,x^\alpha \to \infty$ as $x \to \infty$ if a is positive, and $ax^\alpha \to -\infty$ as $x \to \infty$ if a is negative.

THEOREM 10. *If $f(x)$ has a limit as $x \to \infty$ and if, for all values of $x > A$, we have $f(x) \geqq 0$, then $\lim\limits_{x \to \infty} f(x) \geqq 0$.*

Clearly $f(x)$ does not tend to minus infinity. If $f(x)$ tends to infinity, the result is true if we interpret this limit as being non-negative. If $f(x) \to l$ then, given any positive ε we can find X such that, for all values of $x > X$, we have $|f(x) - l| < \varepsilon$. In particular $f(x) < l + \varepsilon$. Hence, whenever x is greater than *both* X and A, we have $l + \varepsilon > f(x) \geqq 0$. From this it follows that $l > -\varepsilon$, and, since ε may be *any* positive number, we must have $l \geqq 0$.

In this theorem, if we assume as hypothesis that $f(x)$ is definitely positive for $x > A$, we cannot discount the possibility that l may be zero. For example $\dfrac{1}{x} > 0$ for all values of $x > 0$, but $\dfrac{1}{x} \to 0$ as $x \to \infty$.

THEOREM 11. *If $f(x)$, supposed defined for $x > A$, tends to infinity as $x \to \infty$, and if $g(x)$ is bounded below for $x > A$, then $f(x) + g(x) \to \infty$ as $x \to \infty$.*

Let $\underset{x > A}{\underline{\mathrm{Bd}}}\, g(x) = m$. Given any positive number $K(>m)$, we can find a positive number X such that, for all values of $x > X$,

$$f(x) > K - m.$$

For all such values of x, we then have

$$f(x)+g(x)\geqq f(x)+m > K,$$

and the result follows.

Similarly it may be proved that, if $f(x)\to -\infty$ and $f(x)$ is bounded above for $x > X$, then $f(x)+g(x)\to -\infty$.

Example. $\lim_{n\to\infty} \{n^2+(-1)^n\} = \infty$. Here $f_n = n^2 \to \infty$ as $n\to\infty$ and $g_n = (-1)^n$ is bounded below for all positive integers n, the greatest lower bound being -1.

THEOREM 12. *If, as $x\to\infty$, $f(x)\to l_1$ and $g(x)\to l_2$, then*
(i) $f(x)+g(x)\to l_1+l_2$,
(ii) $f(x)-g(x)\to l_1-l_2$.

Given any positive ε, we can find a positive X_1 such that,

$$|f(x)-l_1| < \tfrac{1}{2}\varepsilon$$

whenever $x > X_1$, and we can also find a positive X_2 such that,

$$|g(x)-l_2| < \tfrac{1}{2}\varepsilon$$

whenever $x > X_2$. If X is the larger of X_1 and X_2, we have, for all values of $x > X$,

$$
\begin{aligned}
|\{f(x)+g(x)\}-\{l_1+l_2\}| &= |\{f(x)-l_1\}+\{g(x)-l_2\}| \\
&\leq |f(x)-l_1| + |g(x)-l_2| \\
&< \tfrac{1}{2}\varepsilon+\tfrac{1}{2}\varepsilon = \varepsilon,
\end{aligned}
$$

from which the first result follows. To prove the second we observe that, by Theorem 9, $-g(x)\to -l_2$ as $x\to\infty$. Hence $f(x)-g(x) = f(x)+\{-g(x)\}\to l_1+(-l_2) = l_1-l_2$.

Example.

$$1+ \frac{1}{x^2} \to 1 \text{ as } x\to\infty.$$

THEOREM 13. *If, as $x\to\infty$, $f_1(x)$, $f_2(x)$, ... $f_n(x)$ tend respectively to l_1, l_2, ... l_n, then*

$$f_1(x)+f_2(x)+...+f_n(x)\to l_1+l_2+...+l_n.$$

By the first part of Theorem 12, the result holds for two functions. Suppose that it holds for p functions, that is, we suppose that, in particular,

$$f_1(x)+f_2(x)+\ldots+f_p(x)\to l_1+l_2+\ldots+l_p.$$

Then, for any other function $f_{p+1}(x)$, say,

$$f_1(x)+\ldots+f_p(x)+f_{p+1}(x) = \{f_1(x)+\ldots+f_p(x)\}+f_{p+1}(x)$$
$$\to(l_1+l_2+\ldots+l_p)+l_{p+1},$$

by the assumption and by Theorem 12, and this is equal to

$$l_1+l_2+\ldots+l_{p+1}.$$

The result follows by the Principle of Mathematical Induction.

Example.

$$2+\frac{3}{x}-\frac{2}{x^2}+\frac{5}{x^3}\to2 \text{ as } x\to\infty.$$

THEOREM 14. *If, for $x>A$, $f(x)\leqq g(x)$, and if $f(x)\to\infty$ as $x\to\infty$, then $g(x)\to\infty$ as $x\to\infty$. If $g(x)\to-\infty$ as $x\to\infty$, then $f(x)\to-\infty$ as $x\to\infty$.*

It is sufficient to prove the first of these, since the second follows by considering $-f(x)$ and $-g(x)$.

Since $f(x)\to\infty$ as $x\to\infty$, given any positive number K, we can find a positive X_1, such that $f(x)>K$ whenever $x>X_1$. Let X be the larger of X_1 and A. Then, whenever $x>X$, we have

$$g(x)\geqq f(x)>K,$$

and the result follows.

THEOREM 15. *If, for $x>A$, $f(x)\leqq g(x)$ and if $f(x)\to l_1$ as $x\to\infty$ and $g(x)\to l_2$ as $x\to\infty$, then $l_1\leqq l_2$.*

From Theorem 12 (ii) the function $g(x)-f(x)$ tends to l_2-l_1, and since, for $x>A$, $g(x)-f(x)\geqq0$, it follows from Theorem 10, that $l_2\geqq l_1$.

THEOREM 16. *If $f(x)$ and $g(x)$, supposed defined for $x > A$, are such that $f(x) \to \infty$ as $x \to \infty$ and $\underline{\mathrm{Bd}}\, g(x) > 0$, then $f(x)g(x) \to \infty$ as $x \to \infty$.*

Let $\underline{\mathrm{Bd}}\, g(x) = m$. Given any positive number K, we can find a positive X such that, whenever $x > X$, $f(x) > K/m$. For all such values of x, it follows that

$$f(x)g(x) > \frac{K}{m} \cdot m = K,$$

and we have the required result.

It is clear that the same conclusion follows if $g(x)$ tends to a positive limit as $x \to \infty$ since, if $g(x) \to l (> 0)$, given any number k such that $0 < k < l$, we can find a positive B such that $g(x) > k$ for all values of $x > B$. This number k takes the place of m, and we consider only values of x greater than both A and B.

THEOREM 17. *If $f(x)$ and $g(x)$ have limits l_1 and l_2 respectively as $x \to \infty$, then $f(x)g(x)$ has limit $l_1 l_2$.*

Given a positive number δ, we can find a positive number X_1 such that, whenever $x > X_1$,

$$|f(x) - l_1| < \delta,$$

and we can also find a positive X_2 such that, whenever $x > X_2$,

$$|g(x) - l_2| < \delta.$$

If X is the larger of X_1 and X_2, these inequalities hold simultaneously for all values of $x > X$. For such values of x, we then have

$$
\begin{aligned}
|f(x)g(x) - l_1 l_2| &= |\{f(x) - l_1\}g(x) + l_1\{g(x) - l_2\}| \\
&\leq |\{f(x) - l_1\}g(x)| + |l_1\{g(x) - l_2\}| \\
&= |f(x) - l_1|\,|g(x)| + |l_1|\,|g(x) - l_2| \\
&< |g(x)|\,\delta + |l_1|\,\delta,
\end{aligned}
$$

and, since $g(x) < l_2 + \delta$, we have

$$|g(x)| < |l_2| + |\delta| = |l_2| + \delta,$$

so that

$$|f(x)g(x) - l_1 l_2| < \delta\{|l_1| + |l_2|\} + \delta^2.$$

Now choose any positive number ε. Let the above δ be the positive root of the equation

$$x^2 + x\{|l_1| + |l_2|\} - \varepsilon = 0.$$

That this equation has a positive root follows from the fact that the product of the roots is negative. Having calculated δ we then, in turn, calculate X. It follows that, whenever $x > X$,

$$|f(x)g(x) - l_1 l_2| < \delta\{|l_1| + |l_2|\} + \delta^2 = \varepsilon,$$

and we have the required result.

THEOREM 18.   *If, as $x \to \infty$, $f_1(x)$, $f_2(x)$, ... $f_n(x)$ have limits l_1, l_2, ..., l_n respectively, then $f_1(x), f_2(x), ... f_n(x)$ has limit $l_1 l_2 ... l_n$.*

By Theorem 17, the result holds for any two functions. Suppose that it holds for any p functions. We then have, in particular,

$$f_1(x) f_2(x) ... f_p(x) \to l_1 l_2 ... l_p.$$

For any additional function $f_{p+1}(x)$, we then have

$$f_1(x) f_2(x) ... f_p(x) f_{p+1}(x) = \{f_1(x) f_2(x) ... f_p(x)\} f_{p+1}(x)$$
$$\to (l_1 l_2 ... l_p) l_{p+1},$$

by the assumption and by Theorem 17. This is equal to $l_1 l_2 ... l_{p+1}$, and the result then follows from the Principle of Induction.

THEOREM 19.   *If, as $x \to \infty$, $f(x)$ tends to infinity or to minus infinity, then $\dfrac{1}{f(x)}$ tends to zero.*

Choose any positive number ε, and let K denote $1/\varepsilon$. Then, if $f(x)\to\infty$ as $x\to\infty$, we can find a positive X, such that $f(x)>K=1/\varepsilon$ for all values of $x>X$. Since $f(x)$ is positive for such values of x, it follows that

$$\left|\frac{1}{f(x)}\right| = \frac{1}{f(x)} < \frac{1}{K} = \varepsilon,$$

and we have the first result. The case when $f(x)\to-\infty$ may be dealt with similarly.

Example 4. If α is any positive rational real number and a is any real number, then $ax^{-\alpha}$ tends to zero as $x\to\infty$.

This follows from Examples 1 and 3 and Theorem 19, but the result may of course be established independently from the definition of a limit.

THEOREM 20. *If $f(x)\to l$ as $x\to\infty$ where $l\neq0$, then $\frac{1}{f(x)}$ has limit $1/l$.*

Let δ be a positive number less than $\frac{1}{2}|l|$. This choice is possible since $l\neq0$. We can then find a positive X such that, whenever $x>X$,

$$|f(x)-l|<\delta,$$

and this inequality is equivalent to the pair of inequalities

$$l-\delta<f(x)<l+\delta.$$

It follows that, for all values of $x>X$, $f(x)$ cannot be zero, and

$$\left|\frac{1}{f(x)}-\frac{1}{l}\right| = \left|\frac{l-f(x)}{lf(x)}\right| = \frac{|l-f(x)|}{|l||f(x)|} < \frac{\delta}{|l||f(x)|}.$$

However, we also have, whenever $x>X$,

$$|f(x)| \geq |l|-|\delta| = |l|-\delta > \tfrac{1}{2}|l|,$$

by the choice of δ. Hence, whenever $x>X$, we have

$$\left|\frac{1}{f(x)}-\frac{1}{l}\right| < \frac{\delta}{\frac{1}{2}|l|^2}.$$

Now choose *any* positive ε. Let the above δ be the smaller of $\frac{1}{2}\,|\,l\,|$ and $\frac{1}{2}\,|\,l\,|^2\varepsilon$, and calculate the value of X corresponding to this δ. Then, whenever x is greater than that X, we have

$$\left|\frac{1}{f(x)} - \frac{1}{l}\right| < \varepsilon,$$

and the theorem follows.

Example.

$$\frac{x^2}{2x^2+1} \to \tfrac{1}{2} \text{ as } x \to \infty.$$

This follows since

$$\frac{x^2}{2x^2+1} = \frac{1}{2+\dfrac{1}{x^2}},$$

and the denominator of the second expression tends to 2 as $x \to \infty$.

THEOREM 21. *If $f(x)$ and $g(x)$ have respectively limits l_1 and l_2 as $x \to \infty$ and if $l_2 \neq 0$, then $f(x)/g(x)$ has limit l_1/l_2.*

Since $f(x)/g(x)$ may be written in the form

$$f(x) \cdot \frac{1}{g(x)},$$

the result follows at once from Theorems 17 and 20.

Example 5. If α is any rational real number and r is any real number greater than -1, then, as $n \to \infty$,

$$n^\alpha r^n \to \infty, \text{ if } r > 1,$$
$$n^\alpha r^n \to 0, \text{ if } -1 < r < 1.$$

If $r = 1$, $n^\alpha r^n$ reduces to n^α, which tends to infinity if $\alpha > 0$, to 1 if $\alpha = 0$ and to zero if $\alpha < 0$.

The case $r = 1$ has been dealt with in previous examples.

Suppose that $r > 1$ and that, in the first instance, α is a negative integer, say $\alpha = -p$, so that p is a positive integer. Let $a = r - 1$, so that a is positive. Then, if n is any integer greater than $p + 1$, we have, by the Binomial Theorem,

$$n^{\alpha} r^n = n^{-p}(1 + a)^n$$

$$= n^{-p}\left\{1 + \binom{n}{1}a + \binom{n}{2}a^2 + \ldots a^n\right\}$$

$$> n^{-p}\binom{n}{p+1}a^{p+1}$$

$$= \frac{a^{p+1}}{(p+1)!}\frac{n(n-1)\ldots(n-p)}{n^p}$$

$$= \frac{na^{p+1}}{(p+1)!}\left(1 - \frac{1}{n}\right)\left(1 - \frac{2}{n}\right)\ldots\left(1 - \frac{p}{n}\right).$$

Now a and p are fixed, and each factor of the form

$$\left(1 - \frac{v}{n}\right)$$

tends to 1 as $n \to \infty$, by Theorem 12. Hence, by Theorem 18,

$$\left(1 - \frac{1}{n}\right)\left(1 - \frac{2}{n}\right)\ldots\left(1 - \frac{p}{n}\right) \to 1.$$

Since

$$\frac{a^{p+1}}{(p+1)!}n \to \infty \text{ as } n \to \infty,$$

it follows, by Theorem 16, that the whole expression on the right hand side tends to infinity as n tends to infinity. Hence, by Theorem 14, $n^{\alpha} r^n \to \infty$ as $n \to \infty$. If now α is any rational real number there is a negative integer smaller than α. Let it be $-p$. Then for all positive integers n,

$$n^{\alpha} r^n > n^{-p} r^n$$

and, since the expression on the right has been shown to

tend to infinity as n tends to infinity, the expression on the left also does so by Theorem 14.

If now $r = 0$, then $n^\alpha r^n = 0$ for every positive integer n, and so by Theorem 8, $n^\alpha r^n \to 0$ as $n \to \infty$.

Finally, if $-1 < r < 1$, $r \neq 0$, then $|r| < 1$, and we have

$$0 < |n^\alpha r^n| = n^\alpha |r|^n = \frac{1}{n^{-\alpha}\left|\frac{1}{r}\right|^n}.$$

By the result of the first part, the denominator tends to infinity as $n \to \infty$. Hence, by Theorem 19, $|n^\alpha r^n| \to 0$ as $n \to \infty$. Thus, given ε we can find X such that, for all positive integers $n > X$, we have $|n^\alpha r^n| < \varepsilon$. Hence $n^\alpha r^n \to 0$ as $n \to \infty$.

This example shows that, of the two functions of n, n^α and r^n, the latter is the more dominant as $n \to \infty$, in the sense that its behaviour determines the behaviour of the product. Thus, as $n \to \infty$, $n^{1000}(\frac{7}{8})^n$ behaves like $(\frac{7}{8})^n$, that is, it tends to zero.

Example.

$$\lim_{x \to \infty} \frac{2x^3 + 3x}{3x^3 + 5x^2 + 7} = \frac{2}{3}.$$

This follows from Theorems 18 and 21 on writing the expression in the form

$$\frac{2 + \dfrac{3}{x^2}}{3 + \dfrac{5}{x} + \dfrac{7}{x^3}}.$$

3.3. Limits when $x \to -\infty$. The limit of a function $f(x)$ when x tends to $-\infty$ is the limit, when it exists, of the function $f(-y)$ when y tends to infinity. It has to be supposed in this case that $f(x)$ is defined for all values of $x < A$, where A is some fixed number. Since a limit when $x \to -\infty$ is determined by transforming it by means of the substitution $y = -x$ into a limit when $y \to \infty$, the statements of the theorems, proved for limits of the latter type, may be carried over with minor modifications to limits of this new type. The reader should satisfy himself completely on this point.

Remembering the definition of the statement "$f(y) \to \infty$ as $y \to \infty$", the definition of the statement "$f(x) \to \infty$ as $x \to -\infty$" will be as follows :—Given any positive number K, we can find a positive number X, such that $f(x) > K$ for all values of $x < -X$. For the statement "$f(x) \to l$ as $x \to -\infty$" we shall have the following :—Given any positive number ε, we can find a positive number X, such that $|f(x) - l| < \varepsilon$ for all values of $x < -X$. In these cases, we write

$$\lim_{x \to -\infty} f(x) = \infty. \quad \lim_{x \to -\infty} f(x) = l.$$

In a similar manner definitions are easily constructed for

$$\lim_{x \to -\infty} f(x) = -\infty, \qquad \lim_{n \to -\infty} f_n = \infty,$$

$$\lim_{n \to -\infty} f_n = l, \qquad \lim_{n \to -\infty} f_n = -\infty,$$

where, in the last three cases, n takes integral values.

Example.

$$\lim_{x \to -\infty} x^{-5} = 0.$$

3.4. Limits as $x \to a$. The **limit** of a function $f(x)$ **as** x **tends to** a **from the right** is defined to be the limit of

$$f\left(a + \frac{1}{y}\right)$$

as $y \to \infty$, when this latter limit exists. The limit is denoted by

$$\lim_{x \to a+} f(x).$$

In calculating $\lim\limits_{y\to\infty} f\left(a+\dfrac{1}{y}\right)$ it is essential that $f\left(a+\dfrac{1}{y}\right)$ should be defined for all values of $y>A$, where A is some fixed positive number. It follows that, if $\lim\limits_{x\to a+} f(x)$ is to have a chance to exist, $f(x)$ has to be defined for $a<x<a+\dfrac{1}{A}$; in other words, $f(x)$ must be defined in an open interval with a as left hand end-point.

The **limit** of a function $f(x)$ **as** x **tends to** a **from the left** is defined to be the limit of $f\left(a-\dfrac{1}{y}\right)$ as $y\to\infty$, when this latter limit exists. The limit is denoted by

$$\lim_{x\to a-} f(x),$$

and, in order that this may have a chance to exist, it is essential that $f(x)$ should be defined in an open interval with a as right hand end-point.

If the limits

$$\lim_{x\to a+} f(x), \quad \lim_{x\to a-} f(x)$$

both exist and are equal, then $f(x)$ is said to have a **limit as** $x\to a$. If the two limits above are $+\infty$, we write

$$\lim_{x\to a} f(x) = \infty,$$

if they are both $-\infty$, we write

$$\lim_{x\to a} f(x) = -\infty,$$

and, if they are both equal to l, we write

$$\lim_{x\to a} f(x) = l.$$

It is essential, in order that $\lim\limits_{x\to a} f(x)$ should be capable of evaluation, that $f(x)$ should be defined at each point excepting a itself in an interval enclosing a.

Suppose that $\lim_{x \to a} f(x) = l$ and that ε is a given positive number. Then since, in particular, $\lim_{x \to a+} f(x) = l$, we can find a positive Y_1 such that

$$|f(x)-l| = \left|f\left(a+\frac{1}{y}\right) - l\right| < \varepsilon,$$

whenever $y > Y_1$. In other words, $|f(x)-l| < \varepsilon$ for all values of x satisfying $a < x < a + \frac{1}{Y_1}$. Also, since

$$\lim_{x \to a-} f(x) = l,$$

we can find a positive Y_2 such that

$$|f(x)-l| = \left|f\left(a-\frac{1}{y}\right) - l\right| < \varepsilon,$$

whenever $y > Y_2$. In other words, $|f(x)-l| < \varepsilon$ for all values of x satisfying $a - \frac{1}{Y_2} < x < a$. Denoting $\frac{1}{Y_1}$ by η_1 and $\frac{1}{Y_2}$ by η_2, and, by η, the smaller of η_1 and η_2, we then have

$$|f(x)-l| < \varepsilon,$$

for all values of x, except a, satisfying $|x-a| < \eta$, that is, for all x satisfying $0 < |x-a| < \eta$.

Conversely if, given ε, we can find η such that

$$|f(x)-l| < \varepsilon$$

whenever $0 < |x-a| < \eta$, then, in particular, the inequality holds for $a - \eta < x < a$ and for $a < x < a + \eta$. The transformations $x = a - \frac{1}{y}$ and $x = a + \frac{1}{y}$ then give, respectively,

$$\left|f\left(a-\frac{1}{y}\right) - l\right| < \varepsilon \quad \text{and} \quad \left|f\left(a+\frac{1}{y}\right) - l\right| < \varepsilon, \quad \text{whenever}$$

$y > \dfrac{1}{\eta}$. Thus

$$\lim_{x \to a-} f(x) = l, \quad \lim_{x \to a+} f(x) = l,$$

whence $f(x) \to l$ as $x \to a$.

Thus, to say that $f(x) \to l$ as $x \to a$ is to say that, given a positive number ε, we can find a positive number η such that

$$|f(x) - l| < \varepsilon,$$

whenever $0 < |x - a| < \eta$.

Similarly the definition of

$$\lim_{x \to a} f(x) = \infty$$

may be restated as follows. Given any positive number K, we can find a positive number η, such that $f(x) > K$ whenever $0 < |x - a| < \eta$.

Again the definition of

$$\lim_{x \to a} f(x) = -\infty$$

may be restated thus. Given any positive number K, we can find a positive number η, such that $f(x) < -K$ whenever $0 < |x - a| < \eta$.

Since limits when x tends to a are based on limits when y tends to infinity, all the theorems which we have proved for limits of the latter type may be extended to cover limits of the former type. We shall not deal with such extensions in general since, to do so in every case, would involve much repetition of principle with little change in detail. It will be sufficient to discuss one of the theorems by way of illustration.

Suppose we are given that, as $x \to a$, $f(x) \to l_1$ and $g(x) \to l_2$, and that we have to prove that $f(x) + g(x) \to l_1 + l_2$.

One proof directly based on Theorem 12 is as follows :

Since, as $y \to \infty$, $f\left(a + \dfrac{1}{y}\right) \to l_1$ and $g\left(a + \dfrac{1}{y}\right) \to l_2$, we have

$$f\left(a + \frac{1}{y}\right) + g\left(a + \frac{1}{y}\right) \to l_1 + l_2.$$

Hence

$$\lim_{x \to a+} \{f(x) + g(x)\} = l_1 + l_2.$$

Similarly

$$\lim_{x \to a-} \{f(x) + g(x)\} = l_1 + l_2,$$

and the result follows.

Alternatively we may proceed in the following way. Given any positive ε, we can find a positive number η_1 such that, for all values of x, except a, satisfying $|x - a| < \eta_1$,

$$|f(x) - l_1| < \tfrac{1}{2}\varepsilon,$$

and we can find a positive number η_2 such that, for all values of x, except a, satisfying $|x - a| < \eta_2$,

$$|g(x) - l_2| < \tfrac{1}{2}\varepsilon.$$

If η is the smaller of η_1 and η_2, we have, for all values of x, except a, satisfying $|x - a| < \eta$,

$$
\begin{aligned}
|\{f(x) + g(x)\} - (l_1 + l_2)| &= |\{f(x) - l_1\} + \{g(x) - l_2\}| \\
&\leqq |f(x) - l_1| + |g(x) - l_2| \\
&< \tfrac{1}{2}\varepsilon + \tfrac{1}{2}\varepsilon = \varepsilon,
\end{aligned}
$$

and we have the result required. We conclude the chapter with two further theorems, the first of which consists merely of a simple transformation.

THEOREM 22. *If either of the limits*

$$\lim_{x \to a} f(x), \quad \lim_{x' \to b} f(x' + a - b)$$

exists, then so does the other and the two are equal.

D

Put $x = a + \dfrac{1}{y}$, $x' = b + \dfrac{1}{y'}$, and suppose that the first limit exists. Then, in turn, the following limits exist and are equal to one another:—

$$\lim_{x \to a+} f(x), \qquad \lim_{y \to \infty} f\left(a + \frac{1}{y}\right),$$

$$\lim_{y' \to \infty} f\left(a + \frac{1}{y'}\right), \qquad \lim_{x' \to b+} f(x' + a - b).$$

Similarly for limits tending to a and b on the left. When the second limit in the enunciation exists, the argument is similar.

Example.

$$\lim_{x \to 1} \frac{x^2 - 1}{x - 1} = \lim_{x' \to 0} \frac{(x' + 1)^2 - 1}{x'}$$

$$= \lim_{x' \to 0} \frac{x'^2 + 2x'}{x'}$$

$$= \lim_{x' \to 0} (x' + 2) = 2.$$

We are entitled to cancel x' in the second last line since the value of $\dfrac{x'^2 + 2x'}{x'}$ at $x' = 0$ is not to be taken into account in determining the limit when $x' \to 0$. This function has, of course, no value when $x' = 0$.

THEOREM 23. *If*

(i) *$g(x) \to b$ as $x \to a$,*

(ii) *there is a positive number η_0 such that $g(x) \neq b$ for $a - \eta_0 < x < a + \eta_0$, $x \neq a$,*

(iii) *$f(y) \to l$ as $y \to b$,*

then $f\{g(x)\} \to l$ as $x \to a$.

Given any positive ε, we can find δ such that
$$|f(y)-l|<\varepsilon,$$
whenever $|y-b|<\delta$, $y\neq b$. With this δ, we can now find η, which may be taken to be less than η_0, such that
$$|y-b| = |g(x) - b| < \delta,$$
whenever $|x-a|<\eta$, $x\neq a$. For such values of x, $y\neq b$, and we have
$$|f(y)-l| = |f\{g(x)\}-l|<\varepsilon.$$
The result follows.

A similar theorem holds when $x\to\infty$ or $x\to-\infty$.

Example. $\lim\limits_{x\to 0}\sqrt{(x^2+1)} = 1$. This follows since $y = x^2+1\to 1$ as $x\to 0$ and $\sqrt{y}\to 1$ as $y\to 1$.

Examples III

(1) Evaluate the following limits

(i) $\lim\limits_{x\to\infty}\dfrac{3x^4+5x^2-6}{2x^4+x-2}$;

(vi) $\lim\limits_{x\to 0}\dfrac{3x^2+2}{5x^3+3x+1}$;

(ii) $\lim\limits_{x\to-\infty}\dfrac{3x^3-6x+2}{4x^3+2x^2}$;

(vii) $\lim\limits_{x\to\infty}\sqrt[3]{\left(\dfrac{3x^2}{x^2+1}\right)}$;

(iii) $\lim\limits_{x\to 1}\dfrac{x-1}{x^3-1}$;

(viii) $\lim\limits_{x\to\infty}\{\sqrt[3]{(x+a)}-\sqrt[3]{x}\}$;

(iv) $\lim\limits_{x\to a}\dfrac{x^m-a^m}{x-a}$ (m a positive integer);

(ix) $\lim\limits_{x\to 1}\dfrac{x^3-1}{x^2-4x+3}$;

(v) $\lim\limits_{x\to 0}\dfrac{\sqrt{(a+x)}-\sqrt{a}}{x}$;

(x) $\lim\limits_{x\to 2}\dfrac{(x^2-4)(x-2)}{x^3-3x^2+4}$.

(2) Show, by choosing suitable examples, that if, as $x\to 0$, $f(x)\to\infty$ and $g(x)\to 0$, no general conclusion can be drawn about the behaviour of the product $f(x)g(x)$ as $x\to 0$.

(3) If

$$f(x) = \frac{\sqrt{(x+1)}-1}{x}, \quad (x>0),$$

$$= \tfrac{1}{2}(x^3+1), \qquad (x<0),$$

show that $f(x)$ has a limit when $x \to 0$.

(4) If f_n tends to zero as $n \to \infty$ and ϕ_n is bounded for all positive integral values of n, show that $\phi_n f_n \to 0$ as $n \to \infty$.

CHAPTER IV

CONTINUITY AND DIFFERENTIABILITY

4.1. Continuity. This chapter deals with the definitions and elementary properties of continuity and differentiability.

If $f(x)$ is defined in an interval $a \leq x \leq b$, of which x_0 is an interior point, then $f(x)$ is said to be **continuous at the point** x_0, *if*

$$\lim_{x \to x_0} f(x) = f(x_0);$$

in other words, if the limit of $f(x)$ when $x \to x_0$ exists and is equal to the value of $f(x)$ at x_0. We have seen that $\sqrt{(x^2+1)} \to 1$ as $x \to 0$ and this is the value of $\sqrt{(x^2+1)}$ at $x = 0$. Hence $\sqrt{(x^2+1)}$ is continuous at the point 0. It will be recalled that, in calculating $\lim_{x \to x_0} f(x)$, the value of $f(x)$ at the point x_0 was not taken into consideration. The definition of continuity has to be slightly modified at the end-points a and b of the interval. We are said to have continuity of $f(x)$ at a, or, more strictly, on the right at a, if $\lim_{x \to a+} f(x) = f(a)$, and continuity at b, or, more strictly, on the left at b, if $\lim_{x \to b-} f(x) = f(b)$. These definitions of left and right continuity, although explicitly stated for the end-points a and b, apply also to any point within the interval $a \leq x \leq b$ for which $f(x)$ is defined. A function cannot be continuous at a point x_0 unless the function is defined throughout some interval containing x_0, except at the end-points of the interval, in which case the function must be defined in an interval to the right or the left of the end-point in question.

A function is said to be **continuous in an interval** if it is continuous at each point of the interval.

4.2. The continuity of x^α.

THEOREM 24. *If α is any rational real number the function x^α is continuous at all points a for which a^α is defined.*

We have to prove, that $x^\alpha \to a^\alpha$ as $x \to a$, when a^α has a meaning. Suppose first that α is the positive integer m. Then a^m is defined for every value of a. For any such number a, we have $x \to a$ as $x \to a$ and, since the limit of the product of m functions is the product of the limits, we have $x^m \to a^m$ as $x \to a$.

When $\alpha = 0$, a^α is defined for all values of a except zero. For such values of a we have $a^\alpha = 1$ and $x^\alpha = 1$. Hence $x^\alpha \to a^\alpha$ as $x \to a$.

Suppose now that α is a negative integer $-m$, say. Then a^{-m} is defined for all values of a except zero. For any such number a, since $x^m \to a^m$ we have, by Theorem 20, $x^{-m} \to a^{-m}$.

Suppose that $\alpha = 1/q$ where q is a positive integer. Then $a^{1/q}$ is defined for $a \geqq 0$. Suppose first that a is positive. Choose any positive number ε. Then, if $x > a$, the inequality

$$x^{1/q} - a^{1/q} < \varepsilon,$$

is the same as

$$x < (a^{1/q} + \varepsilon)^q,$$

which, in turn, is the same as

$$x - a < (a^{1/q} + \varepsilon)^q - a.$$

If $0 < x < a$, the inequality

$$a^{1/q} - x^{1/q} < \varepsilon,$$

is the same as

$$(a^{1/q} - \varepsilon)^q < x,$$

and this is the same as $a-x<a-(a^{1/q}-\varepsilon)^q$. Thus, for any given ε $(<a^{1/q})$, we have

$$|x^{1/q}-a^{1/q}|<\varepsilon,$$

whenever $|x-a|<\eta$, where η is the smaller of the two numbers

$$(a^{1/q}+\varepsilon)^q-a, \quad a-(a^{1/q}-\varepsilon)^q.$$

Thus $x^{1/q}\to a^{1/q}$ as $x\to a$, $(a\neq0)$. If $a=0$, the first part of this argument is still valid, and we have

$$x^{1/q}\to0 \text{ as } x\to0+,$$

and there is continuity on the right at a.

Suppose finally that $\alpha=\dfrac{p}{q}$ where p and q are integers and q is positive. Then a^α is defined for all values of $a>0$ if p is negative, and for all values of $a\geq0$ if p is positive. Suppose that, in these respective cases, a is such that a^α has a meaning. Now

$$x^{p/q}=(x^{1/q})^p\to(a^{1/q})^p=a^{p/q},$$

by Theorem 23, and the previous parts of the proof.

4.3. Some theorems on continuity.

THEOREM 25. *If $f(x)$ and $g(x)$ are continuous at a point x_0 then so also are*

    (i) $cf(x)$, *where c is any constant,*

    (ii) $f(x)+g(x)$,

    (iii) $f(x)g(x)$,

    (iv) $\dfrac{f(x)}{g(x)}$, *provided that $g(x_0)\neq0$.*

Since, as $x\to x_0$, $f(x)\to f(x_0)$ and $g(x)\to g(x_0)$ these results are immediate consequences of Theorems 9, 12, 17, 21.

Exactly as in the case of limits, the principle of mathematical induction enables us to extend (ii) and (iii) to the case of n functions $f_1(x)$, $f_2(x)$, ..., $f_n(x)$.

Example. The function

$$\frac{\sqrt{x}+\sqrt{x^3}}{x^2-4}$$

is continuous for all values of $x \geqq 0$ except $x = 2$.

Example. The function

$$\frac{x^3-2x^2+5}{x^{\frac{1}{2}}}$$

is continuous for all values of $x > 0$.

THEOREM 26.   *If $y = f(x)$ is continuous at x_0, if $y_0 = f(x_0)$, and if $g(y)$ is continuous at y_0, then $g\{f(x)\}$ is continuous at x_0.*

Since $g(y)$ is continuous at y_0, given a positive ε, we can find δ such that $|g(y)-g(y_0)| < \varepsilon$ for all values of y *including* y_0, satisfying $|y-y_0| < \delta$. With this δ, we can now find η such that $|f(x)-f(x_0)| < \delta$ for all values of x, *including* x_0, satisfying $|x-x_0| < \eta$. Hence

$$|g\{f(x)\}-g\{f(x_0)\}| < \varepsilon$$

whenever $|x-x_0| < \eta$, and the result follows.

It follows from Theorems 25 and 26 and the continuity properties of the function x^α that any function obtained from x^α by the processes of addition, subtraction, multiplication, division and the extraction of roots is continuous at all points where the function is defined.

Example. The functions

$$\frac{x+2}{\sqrt[3]{(x^2+5)}}, \quad \frac{\sqrt[3]{(x^2-4)}}{\sqrt{(x+1)}},$$

are respectively, continuous for all values of x, continuous for $x \geqq 2$.

THEOREM 27. *If $f(x)$ is continuous at a point x_0 and if $f(x_0) > k$, there is an interval $(x_0 - \eta, x_0 + \eta)$ such that, for all values of x in this interval, $f(x) > k$.*

Choose any positive ε less than $f(x_0) - k$. Then we can find a positive η such that

$$|f(x) - f(x_0)| < \varepsilon,$$

whenever $|x - x_0| < \eta$. Hence, for any x in $(x_0 - \eta, x_0 + \eta)$, we have in particular

$$f(x) - f(x_0) > -\varepsilon,$$

giving $\qquad f(x) > f(x_0) - \varepsilon > k,$

which is the result required.

Geometrically, this theorem means that, for a function which is continuous at x_0, the ordinates at points on the graph near x_0 differ but little from the ordinate at x_0.

THEOREM 28. *If $f(x)$ is continuous for $a \leq x \leq b$, if $f(a) = A$, $f(b) = B$, and if C is some number between A and B then $f(x)$ has the value C for some value ξ of x in the interval (a, b).*

We may suppose that $A < C < B$. The set of points x in $[a, b]$, for which $f(x) < C$, is bounded. Let ξ be its least upper bound. Then $f(\xi) = C$. For, if $f(\xi) > C$, there is an interval $(\xi - h, \xi)$ to the left of ξ throughout which $f(x) > C$, and this contradicts the definition of ξ. Again, if $f(\xi) < C$, there is an interval $(\xi, \xi + h)$ to the right of ξ throughout which $f(x) < C$, so that ξ cannot be the upper bound of such x. Thus $f(\xi) = C$, and the theorem is proved.

There may of course be more than one value of x for which $f(x) = C$, but the importance of the theorem is that it enables us to assert the existence of at least one such x. Geometrically, the theorem shows that the graph of a continuous function is without breaks. It can be traced by a pencil on a piece of paper without raising the pencil from the paper.

4.4. Differentiability. If $f(x)$ is defined in an interval $a \leq x \leq b$, of which x_0 is an interior point, and if

$$\lim_{h \to 0} \frac{f(x_0+h)-f(x_0)}{h}$$

exists and is neither $+\infty$ nor $-\infty$, we say that $f(x)$ is differentiable at x_0. The value of this limit, when it exists, is called the differential coefficient or **derivative of $f(x)$ at the point** x_0. If x_0 is the point a, that is, the left hand end-point of the interval in which $f(x)$ is defined, we say that $f(x)$ is **differentiable** at a, if

$$\lim_{h \to 0+} \frac{f(a+h)-f(a)}{h}$$

exists, and is neither $+\infty$ nor $-\infty$. Similarly, we say that $f(x)$ is differentiable at b, if

$$\lim_{h \to 0-} \frac{f(b+h)-f(b)}{h}$$

exists, and is neither $+\infty$ nor $-\infty$.

Just as in the case of continuity, it is necessary, for differentiability at a point x_0, that the function in question be defined in an interval surrounding x_0 except that, in the case of the end-points, the function need only be defined in an interval to the right of the left hand end-point and in an interval to the left of the right hand end-point.

A function $f(x)$ is said to be **differentiable in an interval** if it is differentiable at each point of the interval.

It will now be shown that differentiability at a point implies continuity at that point.

THEOREM 29. *If $f(x)$ is differentiable at a point x_0, then it is continuous at x_0.*

Let the derivative of $f(x)$ at the point x_0 be k; that is,

$$\lim_{h \to 0} \frac{f(x_0 + h) - f(x_0)}{h} = k.$$

Given ε, we can find η such that

$$\left| \frac{f(x_0 + h) - f(x_0)}{h} - k \right| < \varepsilon,$$

whenever $|h| < \eta$. For such values of h, we have

$$\left| \frac{f(x_0 + h) - f(x_0)}{h} \right| - |k| < \varepsilon,$$

and this is the same as

$$|f(x_0 + h) - f(x_0)| < |h| \{|k| + \varepsilon\}.$$

Let $h \to 0$. Then, since ε, k are fixed, the right hand side tends to zero. Hence $f(x_0 + h) \to f(x_0)$ as $h \to 0$, and this is the same as saying that $f(x) \to f(x_0)$ as $x \to x_0$. Thus $f(x)$ is continuous at x_0.

The converse of this theorem is not true. It is quite easy to construct a function which is continuous at a point and not differentiable at that point. For example, $|x|$ is continuous at the point $x = 0$, but is not differentiable there, since, when $h > 0$,

$$\frac{|h| - 0}{h} = 1 \to 1 \text{ as } h \to 0,$$

and, when $h < 0$,

$$\frac{|h| - 0}{h} = -1 \to -1 \text{ as } h \to 0.$$

The derivative of $f(x)$ at a point x_0 is usually denoted by symbols such as

$$\frac{d}{dx} \left\{ f(x) \right\}_{x = x_0}, \quad f'(x_0), \quad D \left\{ f(x) \right\}_{x = x_0}.$$

4.5. Fundamental theorems on differentiation. Before dealing with the usual theorems on differentiation it will be noted that, from the definition, a constant k is differentiable with respect to x in any interval and that its derivative is zero.

THEOREM 30. *If $f(x)$ and $g(x)$ are differentiable at x_0 then so are $cf(x)$, where c is independent of x, $f(x)+g(x)$, $f(x)g(x)$, and $\dfrac{f(x)}{g(x)}$, provided that, in the last case, $g(x_0)\neq 0$.*

Also

(i) $\dfrac{d}{dx}\left\{cf(x)\right\}_{x=x_0} = cf'(x_0),$

(ii) $\dfrac{d}{dx}\left\{f(x)+g(x)\right\}_{x=x_0} = f'(x_0)+g'(x_0),$

(iii) $\dfrac{d}{dx}\left\{f(x)g(x)\right\}_{x=x_0} = f(x_0)g'(x_0)+f'(x_0)g(x_0),$

(iv) $\dfrac{d}{dx}\left\{\dfrac{f(x)}{g(x)}\right\}_{x=x_0} = \dfrac{g(x_0)f'(x_0)-f(x_0)g'(x_0)}{\{g(x_0)\}^2}$

(i) We have

$$\frac{cf(x_0+h)-cf(x_0)}{h} = c\left\{\frac{f(x_0+h)-f(x_0)}{h}\right\},$$

and the right hand side tends to $cf'(x_0)$ as $h\to 0$. Hence $cf(x)$ is differentiable at x_0, and its derivative is as stated.

(ii) We have

$$\frac{\{f(x_0+h)+g(x_0+h)\}-\{f(x_0)+g(x_0)\}}{h}$$
$$= \frac{f(x_0+h)-f(x_0)}{h} + \frac{g(x_0+h)-g(x_0)}{h},$$

and the right hand side, by hypothesis, tends to

$$f'(x_0) + g'(x_0)$$

as $h \to 0$. Hence $f(x) + g(x)$ is differentiable at x_0, and its derivative is as stated.

(iii) We have

$$\frac{f(x_0 + h)g(x_0 + h) - f(x_0)g(x_0)}{h}$$

$$= f(x_0 + h)\frac{\{g(x_0 + h) - g(x_0)\}}{h} + g(x_0)\frac{\{f(x_0 + h) - f(x_0)\}}{h}.$$

As $h \to 0$, $f(x_0 + h) \to f(x_0)$, since $f(x)$, being differentiable at x_0, is continuous at x_0. It follows, by hypothesis, that the right hand side tends to

$$f(x_0)g'(x_0) + g(x_0)f'(x_0).$$

Hence $f(x)g(x)$ is differentiable at x_0, and its derivative at x_0 is as stated.

(iv) Since $g(x_0) \neq 0$ and since $g(x)$, being differentiable at x_0, is also continuous at x_0, there is an interval $(x_0 - \eta, x_0 + \eta)$ within which $g(x) \neq 0$. Choose any h such that $|h| < \eta$.
Then, for such h,

$$\frac{\dfrac{f(x_0 + h)}{g(x_0 + h)} - \dfrac{f(x_0)}{g(x_0)}}{h} = \frac{f(x_0 + h)g(x_0) - f(x_0)g(x_0 + h)}{hg(x_0)g(x_0 + h)}$$

$$= \frac{g(x_0)\{f(x_0 + h) - f(x_0)\} - f(x_0)\{g(x_0 + h) - g(x_0)\}}{hg(x_0)g(x_0 + h)}$$

$$\to \frac{g(x_0)f'(x_0) - f(x_0)g'(x_0)}{\{g(x_0)\}^2},$$

as $h \to 0$. Hence $\dfrac{f(x)}{g(x)}$ is differentiable at x_0, and its derivative at x_0 is as stated.

The results (ii) and (iii) of the last theorem may be extended immediately by the principle of mathematical induction. Thus, if $f_1(x), f_2(x), \ldots, f_n(x)$ are differentiable at x_0, so also are

$$f_1(x) + f_2(x) + \ldots + f_n(x),$$
$$f_1(x) f_2(x) \ldots f_n(x),$$

and

$$\frac{d}{dx}\left\{\sum_{r=1}^{n} f_r(x)\right\}_{x=x_0} = \sum_{r=1}^{n} f_r'(x_0),$$

$$\frac{d}{dx}\left\{\prod_{r=1}^{n} f_r(x)\right\}_{x=x_0} = \sum_{r=1}^{n} f_1(x_0)f_2(x_0)\ldots f_r'(x_0)\ldots f_n(x_0).$$

The notation $\sum_{r=1}^{n} a_r$ means simply that we give r all possible integral values between 1 and n, both inclusive, and add. The notation $\prod_{r=1}^{n} a_r$ means that we give r all possible integral values between 1 and n, both inclusive, and then multiply. Thus

$$\sum_{r=1}^{n} a_r = a_1 + a_2 + \ldots + a_n, \quad \prod_{r=1}^{n} a_r = a_1 a_2 \ldots a_n.$$

THEOREM 31. *If $y = f(x)$ is differentiable at x_0, if $y_0 = f(x_0)$ and if $g(y)$ is differentiable at y_0, then $g\{f(x)\}$ is differentiable at x_0, and*

$$\frac{d}{dx}\left\{g[f(x)]\right\}_{x=x_0} = g'(y_0)f'(x_0).$$

Suppose first that $f'(x_0) \neq 0$. Choose ε so that $f'(x_0) - \varepsilon$ and $f'(x_0) + \varepsilon$ have the same sign. Then we can find η such that

$$f'(x_0) - \varepsilon < \frac{f(x_0 + h) - f(x_0)}{h} < f'(x_0) + \varepsilon,$$

whenever $|h| < \eta$. We may suppose that η is small enough to ensure $f(x)$ and $g\{f(x)\}$ are defined in $|x - x_0| < \eta$. For such values of h, $f(x_0 + h) - f(x_0)$ is not zero. Let $k = f(x_0 + h) - f(x_0)$. Then, for $|h| < \eta$,

$$\frac{g\{f(x_0 + h)\} - g\{f(x_0)\}}{h} = \frac{g(y_0 + k) - g(y_0)}{k} \cdot \frac{k}{h}$$

$$= \frac{g(y_0 + k) - g(y_0)}{k} \cdot \frac{f(x_0 + h) - f(x_0)}{h}.$$

As $h \to 0$ the second factor on the right tends to $f'(x_0)$. Moreover $k \to 0$ as $h \to 0$, since $f(x)$ is continuous at x_0. Thus, as $h \to 0$, the right hand side tends to $g'(y_0)f'(x_0)$, giving the result required.

Suppose now that $f'(x_0) = 0$. Let $(x_0 - \delta, x_0 + \delta)$ be an interval surrounding x_0, within which $f(x)$ and $g\{f(x)\}$ are defined. In this interval there may be points $x_0 + h$ for which $f(x_0 + h) = f(x_0)$ and there may be points $x_0 + h$ for which $f(x_0 + h) \neq f(x_0)$. For values of h in the first category

$$g\{f(x_0 + h)\} - g\{f(x_0)\} = 0$$

and for values of h in the second, we proceed as in the first part of the theorem and note that as $h \to 0$ through these particular values

$$\frac{f(x_0 + h) - f(x_0)}{h} \to 0.$$

4.6. The derivative of x^α. We suppose that α is a rational real number, since x^α has not so far been defined for more general α.

THEOREM 32. *If α is any rational real number the function x^α is differentiable at all points a where the derivative is defined. The derivative at such a point a is*

$$\alpha a^{\alpha - 1}, \quad (\alpha \neq 0, 1),$$
$$0, \quad (\alpha = 0),$$
$$1, \quad (\alpha = 1).$$

When $\alpha = 0$, 1, the proof is immediate. We now consider the other cases.

Case (i). Suppose that α is the positive integer m $(m \neq 1)$. Then x^{m-1} is defined for all values of x. Let a be any such value. Then, for any real number $h \neq 0$,

$$\frac{(a+h)^m - a^m}{h} = \frac{a^m + \binom{m}{1}ha^{m-1} + \binom{m}{2}h^2 a^{m-2} + \dots + h^m - a^m}{h}$$

$$= ma^{m-1} + \binom{m}{2}ha^{m-2} + \dots + h^{m-1}$$

$$\to ma^{m-1} = \alpha a^{\alpha-1},$$

as $h \to 0$, by Theorem 13.

Case (ii). Suppose that α is the negative integer $-m$. Then x^{-m-1} is defined for all values of x except zero. Let a be such a value of x. Then, by Theorem 30 (iv),

$$\frac{d}{dx}\left\{x^{-m}\right\}_{x=a} = \frac{d}{dx}\left\{\frac{1}{x^m}\right\}_{x=a}$$

$$= \frac{-ma^{m-1}}{a^{2m}} = -ma^{-m-1} = \alpha a^{\alpha-1},$$

which is the required result.

Case (iii). Suppose that α is the rational number $1/q$, where q is a positive integer. Then $x^{1/q-1}$ is defined for positive values of x. Let a be such a value, and let h be any real number such that $a+h > 0$, $h \neq 0$. In the identity

$$y^n - b^n = (y-b)(y^{n-1} + y^{n-2}b + \dots + yb^{n-2} + b^{n-1}),$$

(n a positive integer), which may be verified by direct multiplication of the right hand side, put

$$y = (a+h)^{1/q}, \quad b = a^{1/q}, \quad n = q.$$

We obtain

$$\frac{(a+h)^{1/q}-a^{1/q}}{h} = \frac{(a+h)-a}{h\{(a+h)^{1-(1/q)}+(a+h)^{1-(2/q)}a^{1/q}++a^{1-(1/q)}\}}$$

$$= \frac{1}{(a+h)^{1-(1/q)}+(a+h)^{1-(2/q)}a^{(1/q)}+\ldots+a^{1-(1/q)}}$$

$$\rightarrow \frac{1}{qa^{1-(1/q)}} = \frac{1}{q}a^{(1/q)-1} = \alpha a^{\alpha-1},$$

as $h\rightarrow 0$, by Theorems 13, 20 and 24.

Case (iv). Suppose that α is a rational number of the form p/q, where p, q are integers and q is positive. If $p/q > 1$, $x^{(p/q)-1}$ is defined for all $x \geq 0$ while, if $p/q < 1$, it is defined for all $x > 0$. Suppose that $a > 0$. Then, since

$$x^{p/q} = (x^{1/q})^p,$$

we have, by Theorem 31,

$$\frac{d}{dx}\left\{x^{p/q}\right\}_{x=a} = p(x^{1/q})^{p-1}\frac{1}{q}a^{(1/q)-1}$$

$$= \frac{p}{q}a^{(p/q)-1} = \alpha a^{\alpha-1}.$$

If $p/q > 1$, $x^{p/q}$ is differentiable at $x = 0$ and the derivative is zero, for

$$\lim_{h\to 0}\frac{h^{p/q}}{h} = \lim_{h\to 0}h^{(p/q)-1} = 0,$$

by Theorem 24.

Example.

$$D\{(1-x^2)^{\frac{1}{2}}\} = \tfrac{1}{2}(1-x^2)^{-\frac{1}{2}}\cdot-2x$$

$$= \frac{-x}{(1-x^2)^{\frac{1}{2}}},$$

for all values of x such that $-1 < x < 1$.

E

Example.

$$D\{(1-x^2)^{\frac{3}{2}}\} = \tfrac{3}{2} \cdot (1-x^2)^{\frac{1}{2}} \cdot -2x$$
$$= -3x(1-x^2)^{\frac{1}{2}},$$

for all values of x such that $-1 \leqq x \leqq 1$.

Examples IV

(1) Find the derivatives at the point x for the following functions of x, and state for what values of x the differentiations are valid.

(i) $\sqrt{\left(\dfrac{2x+1}{x-1}\right)}$; (ii) $x\sqrt{(1-x^2)}$; (iii) $\sqrt[3]{(3x^4+2x^2)}$;

(iv) $\dfrac{x^2-1}{2x^3+1}$; (v) $(x^{\frac{3}{2}}+1)^{\frac{3}{2}}$; (vi) $\dfrac{x}{\sqrt[3]{(x^2-4)}}$.

(2) Show that the function

$$f(x) = 0, \qquad (0 \leqq x < 1),$$
$$= 1-x^2, \quad (1 \leqq x < 2),$$

is not differentiable at the point $x = 1$, but that the function

$$f(x) = 0, \qquad (0 \leqq x < 1),$$
$$= (1-x)^2, \quad (1 \leqq x \leqq 2),$$

is differentiable at this point.

(3) What value must be given to the function

$$f(x) = x, \quad (0 \leqq x < 1),$$
$$= x^3, \quad (1 < x \leqq 2),$$

at the point $x = 1$, to ensure continuity at this point ?

(4) The function $f(x)$ is given to be continuous for $0 \leqq x \leqq 1$ and is defined, for $0 < x < 1$, to be

$$\frac{x(1-x)}{2-x-x^2}.$$

Find $f(0)$ and $f(1)$.

(5) For what values of x are the following functions continuous ?

(i) $\dfrac{\sqrt{(x-1)}}{x^2-2}$;

(ii) $\dfrac{x^2-1}{\sqrt{(x^2-4)}}$;

(iii) $\sqrt[3]{\left\{\dfrac{x+1}{x^2-9}\right\}}$;

(iv) $\dfrac{x^3+x^2-1}{\sqrt{(x+2)}}$.

(6) Show that the function

$$f(x)=\sum_{r=1}^{n}|x-r|^3$$

is continuous for all values of x, and differentiable for all values of x except the values 1, 2, ..., n.

CHAPTER V

THE EXPONENTIAL AND LOGARITHMIC FUNCTIONS

5.1. Monotonic functions. Before discussing the particular functions which form the subject matter of this chapter, we consider briefly the class of functions which are called monotonic.

A function $f(x)$, defined in an interval $a \leq x \leq b$, is said to be monotonic increasing in this interval if, as x increases from a to b, $f(x)$ does not decrease. More precisely, $f(x)$ is said to be **monotonic increasing** in a set E if, when x_1 and x_2 are *any* members of the set with $x_1 < x_2$, then $f(x_1) \leq f(x_2)$. A function $f(x)$ is said to be **monotonic decreasing** in a set E if, when x_1 and x_2 are any members of the set with $x_1 < x_2$, then $f(x_1) \geq f(x_2)$.

For example, the function $1/x$ is monotonic decreasing for $x > 0$, and $1 - \dfrac{1}{n}$ is a monotonic increasing function of n for all positive integral values of n.

We have seen that a function $f(x)$ defined for $x \geq A$, need not have a limit when $x \to \infty$. However, in the case when $f(x)$ is monotonic, a limit does in fact exist. The limit may be $+\infty$ or $-\infty$. A limit which is neither $+\infty$ nor $-\infty$ is said to be a **finite limit**.

THEOREM 33. *If, for $x \geq A$, $f(x)$ is monotonic, then $f(x)$ has a limit when $x \to \infty$.*

Suppose that $f(x)$ is monotonic increasing.

Either $f(x)$ is bounded above for $x \geq A$, or $f(x)$ is not bounded above for $x \geq A$. Suppose that it is bounded

above. Let $\overline{\mathrm{Bd}}\ f(x) = l$. Then, given any positive ε,
$\begin{subarray}{c} x \geq A \end{subarray}$
there is a value X of x for which $f(X) > l - \varepsilon$. Since $f(x)$ is monotonic increasing it follows that, for all values of $x > X$,

$$f(x) \geq f(X) > l - \varepsilon.$$

But, for $x \geq A$, and, in particular, for $x > X$,

$$f(x) \leq l < l + \varepsilon.$$

Hence, whenever $x > X$, we have $|f(x) - l| < \varepsilon$, and therefore $f(x) \to l$ as $x \to \infty$.

If $f(x)$ is not bounded above, then, given any positive number K, there is a value X of x, for which $f(X) > K$. Since $f(x)$ is increasing, it follows that $f(x) \geq f(X) > K$ for all values of $x > X$. Hence $f(x) \to \infty$ as $x \to \infty$.

Similarly, when $f(x)$ is monotonic decreasing for $x \geq A$, it may be proved that $f(x)$ tends either to $-\infty$ or to a limit l as $x \to \infty$, depending on whether $f(x)$ has not or has a lower bound for $x \geq A$.

The same theorem applies in the case of the positive integral variable n on replacing x by n throughout.

THEOREM 34. *If, for all values of $x < a$, $f(x)$ is monotonic, then $f(x)$ has a limit when x tends to a from the left.*

If $x_1 < x_2 < a$ we have, if $f(x)$ is monotonic increasing,

$$f(x_1) \leq f(x_2).$$

Put $x = a - \dfrac{1}{y}$, $y > 0$, $x_1 = a - \dfrac{1}{y_1}$, $x_2 = a - \dfrac{1}{y_2}$. Then,

since $x_1 < x_2$, we have $y_1 < y_2$, and $f\left(a - \dfrac{1}{y}\right)$ is monotonic

increasing. By Theorem 33 this has a limit when $y \to \infty$ which, by definition, is $\lim_{x \to a-} f(x)$. A similar proof holds when $f(x)$ is monotonic decreasing.

Similarly, if $f(x)$ is monotonic for $x > a$, it is easy to prove that $\lim_{x \to a+} f(x)$ exists.

We sometimes use the terms **monotonic strictly increasing,** or **monotonic strictly decreasing,** in connection with a function $f(x)$ defined in a set E. In the former case, if x_1 and x_2 are any members of the set with $x_1 < x_2$, then $f(x_1) < f(x_2)$, and, in the latter, $f(x_1) > f(x_2)$.

THEOREM 35. *If $y = f(x)$ is a monotonic continuous function which increases strictly from A to B as x increases from a to b, then the relation $y = f(x)$ defines x as a monotonic continuous function of y which increases strictly from a to b as y increases from A to B.*

Let λ be any real number such that $A \leqq \lambda \leqq B$. By Theorem 28, $f(x)$ takes the value λ for some value ξ of x such that $a \leqq \xi \leqq b$. There cannot be more than one such value of x, for, suppose that ξ_1 were another and that $\xi < \xi_1$; then $f(\xi) < f(\xi_1)$, so that both cannot be equal to λ. It follows that, to each number λ in (A, B), there corresponds one number ξ in (a, b) or, to change the notation, to each number y in (A, B) there corresponds one number x in (a, b). Hence x is a function of y defined for $A \leqq y \leqq B$. Let $x = F(y)$.

Let y_1, y_2 be any two numbers in (A, B) with $y_1 < y_2$, and let the corresponding values of x be x_1 and x_2. Then $x_1 < x_2$, for, if $x_1 \geqq x_2$, we would have $f(x_1) \geqq f(x_2)$, that is, $y_1 \geqq y_2$. It follows that $F(y)$ increases strictly from a to b as y increases from A to B.

Let y_0, $y_0 + k$ be any two points in (A, B) and let $x_0 = F(y_0)$, $x_0 + h = F(y_0 + k)$. Then $y_0 = f(x_0)$,

$$y_0 + k = f(x_0 + h).$$

To prove continuity of $F(y)$ at y_0 we have to show that $h \to 0$ as $k \to 0$. Suppose $k > 0$ and that $k \to 0+$. Then h is a monotonic positive function of k and therefore tends to a limit l ($\geqq 0$) as $k \to 0+$. If $l > 0$,

$$f(x_0) = y_0 = \lim_{k \to 0} (y_0 + k) = f(x_0 + l),$$

by the continuity of $f(x)$. This provides a contradiction, since $f(x)$ is strictly increasing. Hence $l = 0$, and the continuity of $F(y)$ on the right at y_0 follows. Similarly, it may be shown that $F(y)$ is continuous on the left at y_0, so that $F(y)$ is continuous at y_0. But y_0 was any point of (A, B). Hence $F(y)$ is continuous throughout this interval.

THEOREM 36. *With the hypothesis of Theorem 35, if $f(x)$ is differentiable at x_0, $y_0 = f(x_0)$ and if $x = F(y)$, $f'(x_0) \neq 0$, then $F(y)$ is differentiable at y_0, and*

$$F'(y_0) = 1/[f'(x_0)].$$

Let $y_0 + k$ be any point in (A, B) and let $x_0 + h$ be the corresponding point in (a, b). Then $h \to 0$ as $k \to 0$, and

$$\frac{F(y_0 + k) - F(y_0)}{k} = \frac{(x_0 + h) - x_0}{f(x_0 + h) - f(x_0)} = \frac{h}{f(x_0 + h) - f(x_0)} \to \frac{1}{f'(x_0)}$$

as $k \to 0$, if $f'(x_0) \neq 0$. The result follows.

5.2. The exponential function. In the discussion which follows we shall frequently use the inequality

$$1 + r + r^2 + \ldots + r^{n-1} = \sum_{\nu=0}^{n-1} r^\nu = \frac{1 - r^n}{1 - r} < \frac{1}{1 - r}, \qquad (A)$$

where $0 < r < 1$. The first of these relations is a matter of notation, the second simply states the sum of the first n terms of the standard geometrical progression, and the third follows since $r^n/(1 - r)$ is positive when $0 < r < 1$.

We first consider an important limit.

THEOREM 37. *If x is any real number, the function*

$$f_n(x) = \left(1 + \frac{x}{n}\right)^n$$

tends to a finite limit when $n \to \infty$.

We divide the proof into three cases.

Case (i) $x = 0$. In this case $f_n(0) = 1$ for every positive integer n, so that $\lim_{n \to \infty} f_n(0) = 1$.

Case (ii) $x > 0$. From the Binomial Theorem,

$$f_n(x) = 1 + \sum_{r=1}^{n} \binom{n}{r} \left(\frac{x}{n}\right)^r$$

$$= 1 + \sum_{r=1}^{n} \left(1 - \frac{1}{n}\right)\left(1 - \frac{2}{n}\right) \ldots \left(1 - \frac{r-1}{n}\right)\frac{x^r}{r!}$$

$$< 1 + \sum_{r=1}^{n} \left(1 - \frac{1}{n+1}\right)\left(1 - \frac{2}{n+1}\right) \ldots \left(1 - \frac{r-1}{n+1}\right)\frac{x^r}{r!}$$

$$< f_{n+1}(x),$$

from which it follows that, for each $x > 0$, $f_n(x)$ is a monotonic increasing function of n.

We proceed to prove that $f_n(x)$ is bounded above for all positive integers n and for each fixed $x > 0$. Let p denote the integer next greater than x if x is not an integer, and let p denote x if x is an integer. We then have

$$f_n(x) = 1 + \sum_{r=1}^{n} \left(1 - \frac{1}{n}\right)\left(1 - \frac{2}{n}\right) \ldots \left(1 - \frac{r-1}{n}\right)\frac{x^r}{r!} \qquad (B)$$

$$< 1 + \sum_{r=1}^{n} \frac{x^r}{r!},$$

and so

$$f_n(x) \leqq 1 + \sum_{r=1}^{p} \frac{x^r}{r!}$$

when $n \leqq p$. When $n > p$, we may write

$$f_n(x) \leqq \left\{1 + \frac{x}{1!} + \ldots + \frac{x^{p-1}}{(p-1)!}\right\} + \left\{\frac{p^p}{p!} + \frac{p^{p+1}}{(p+1)!} + \ldots + \frac{p^n}{n!}\right\}$$

$$= \left\{1 + \frac{x}{1!} + \ldots + \frac{x^{p-1}}{(p-1)!}\right\} + \frac{p^p}{p!}\left\{1 + \ldots + \frac{p^{n-p}}{(p+1)\ldots n}\right\}$$

$$< \left\{ 1 + \frac{x}{1!} + \dots + \frac{x^{p-1}}{(p-1)!} \right\}$$

$$+ \frac{p^p}{p!} \left\{ 1 + \frac{p}{p+1} + \left(\frac{p}{p+1} \right)^2 + \dots + \left(\frac{p}{p+1} \right)^{n-p} \right\}$$

$$< \left\{ 1 + \frac{x}{1!} + \dots + \frac{x^{p-1}}{(p-1)!} \right\} + \frac{p^p}{p!} \frac{1}{1 - \frac{p}{p+1}} \qquad (C)$$

by (A). It follows that, for any given positive x, $f_n(x)$ is bounded above for all positive integers n. Hence $f_n(x)$ tends to a finite limit as $n \to \infty$.

Case (iii) $x < 0$. Write $y = -x$, so that y is positive. Then

$$\left(1 + \frac{x}{n} \right)^n = \left(1 - \frac{y}{n} \right)^n = \frac{\left\{ 1 - \frac{y^2}{n^2} \right\}^n}{\left\{ 1 + \frac{y}{n} \right\}^n}.$$

When $n \to \infty$ the denominator of this expression tends to a limit which is not zero. The numerator may be written

$$1 - \frac{y^2}{n} + \frac{n(n-1)}{1.2} \left(\frac{y^2}{n^2} \right)^2 + \dots + (-1)^n \left(\frac{y^2}{n^2} \right)^n = 1 + R_n,$$

say, where

$$|R_n| \leqq \frac{y^2}{n} + \frac{y^4}{n^2} + \frac{y^6}{n^3} + \dots + \frac{y^{2n}}{n^n} < \frac{\frac{y^2}{n}}{1 - \frac{y^2}{n}} = \frac{y^2}{n - y^2},$$

by inequality (A), for all values of $n > y^2$. Thus, for each fixed $x < 0$, $R_n \to 0$ as $n \to \infty$, and the result follows.

The limit of the expression $\left(1 + \frac{x}{n} \right)^n$ when $n \to \infty$, which exists for every value of x, will be a function of x. It is called the **exponential function** of x and is denoted by exp x. We have seen, in the course of the proof of Theorem 37, that

$$\exp 0 = 1, \quad \exp x \cdot \exp(-x) = 1.$$

Further properties of this exponential function follow readily.

THEOREM 38. *If x_1, x_2 are any real numbers*

$$\exp x_1 \cdot \exp x_2 = \exp(x_1 + x_2).$$

The result has already been obtained in the case when $x_1 + x_2 = 0$. Suppose that $x_1 + x_2 > 0$. Then, if $n > |x_1 x_2|$,

$$\left(1 + \frac{x_1}{n}\right)^n \left(1 + \frac{x_2}{n}\right)^n = \left(1 + \frac{x_1 + x_2}{n} + \frac{x_1 x_2}{n^2}\right)^n$$

$$= \left(1 + \frac{x_1 + x_2}{n}\right)^n$$

$$+ \sum_{r=1}^{n} \binom{n}{r} \left\{1 + \frac{x_1 + x_2}{n}\right\}^{n-r} \left(\frac{x_1 x_2}{n^2}\right)^r$$

$$= \left(1 + \frac{x_1 + x_2}{n}\right)^n + R_n,$$

where

$$|R_n| \leqq \sum_{r=1}^{n} \binom{n}{r} \left(1 + \frac{x_1 + x_2}{n}\right)^{n-r} \left(\frac{|x_1 x_2|}{n^2}\right)^r.$$

Now

$$0 < \frac{1}{n^r} \binom{n}{r} \leqq 1, \quad 0 < \left(1 + \frac{x_1 + x_2}{n}\right)^{-r} < 1$$

and therefore

$$|R_n| < \exp(x_1 + x_2) \sum_{r=1}^{n} \left(\frac{|x_1 x_2|}{n}\right)^r$$

$$< \exp(x_1 + x_2) \frac{|x_1 x_2|}{n - |x_1 x_2|},$$

by inequality (A). Hence $R_n \to 0$ as $n \to \infty$, and the theorem follows.

When $x_1 + x_2 < 0$, put $y_1 = -x_1$, $y_2 = -x_2$. Then $y_1 + y_2 > 0$ and

$$\exp(x_1 + x_2) = \frac{1}{\exp(y_1 + y_2)} - \frac{1}{\exp y_1 \exp y_2}$$
$$= \exp(-y_1)\exp(-y_2) = \exp x_1 \exp x_2.$$

It follows from the Principle of Mathematical Induction that, if x_1, x_2, ..., x_p are any p real numbers,

$$\exp x_1 \exp x_2 ... \exp x_p = \exp(x_1 + x_2 + ... + x_p),$$

and, in particular, that

$$(\exp x)^p = \exp(px),$$

where x is any real number and p is a positive integer.

THEOREM 39. *We have*
  (i) $\exp x \geqq 1$, $(x \geqq 0)$; $0 < \exp x < 1$, $(x < 0)$;
  (ii) $\exp x \to \infty$, $\exp(-x) \to 0$ as $x \to \infty$;
  (iii) $\exp x$ *is a monotonic strictly increasing function of x for all values of x.*

(i) When $x > 0$,

$$f_n(x) = \left(1 + \frac{x}{n}\right)^n > 1$$

and, since $f_n(x)$ increases with n to the limit $\exp x$, it follows that $\exp x > 1$ for such x. When $x = 0$, $\exp x = 1$. When $x < 0$,

$$\exp x = \frac{1}{\exp(-x)},$$

which lies between 0 and 1.

(ii) For any fixed positive integral value of n,

$$\exp x > \left(1 + \frac{x}{n}\right)^n \to \infty$$

as $x \to \infty$. It follows that $\exp(-x) \to 0$ as $x \to \infty$.

(iii) Let x_1, x_1+h be any two values of x, where $h>0$. Then $\exp(x_1+h)-\exp x_1 = \exp x_1(\exp h-1)>0$, by (i) above.

THEOREM 40. *If $0<x<2$, we have*

$$1+x<\exp x\leqq 1+x+\frac{x^2}{2-x}.$$

The first of these inequalities follows at once from (B) since, for $n\geqq 2$, $f_n(x)>1+x$. Also, for any positive integral value of n,

$$f_n(x)<1+x+\sum_{r=2}^{n}\frac{x^r}{r!}$$

$$<1+x+x^2\left(\frac{1}{2}+\frac{x}{2^2}+\frac{x^2}{2^3}+\ldots+\frac{x^{n-2}}{2^{n-1}}\right)$$

$$<1+x+x^2\left(\frac{\dfrac{1}{2}}{1-\dfrac{x}{2}}\right)=1+x+\frac{x^2}{2-x}.$$

Since $f_n(x)$ is a monotonic increasing function of n, the second inequality follows on letting n tend to infinity.

THEOREM 41. *The function $\exp x$ is differentiable (and therefore continuous) for all values of x, and its derivative at the point x is $\exp x$.*

Let x be any real number and h a non-zero real number such that $|h|<2$. Then

$$\frac{\exp(x+h)-\exp x}{h} = \exp x\left(\frac{\exp h-1}{h}\right),$$

and the theorem will be established if we show that, as $h\to 0$,

$$\frac{\exp h-1}{h}\to 1.$$

Suppose first that h is positive. Then, from Theorem 40,

$$1 < \frac{\exp h - 1}{h} < 1 + \frac{h}{2-h},$$

so that

$$\lim_{h \to 0+} \frac{\exp h - 1}{h} = 1.$$

If $h < 0$, write $k = -h$. Then

$$\frac{\exp h - 1}{h} = \frac{(1/\exp k) - 1}{-k} = \frac{\exp k - 1}{k \exp k}.$$

Now, from the first part,

$$\frac{\exp k - 1}{k} \to 1$$

as $k \to 0+$ and, from Theorem 40, $\exp k \to 1$ as $k \to 0+$. Thus

$$\lim_{h \to 0-} \frac{\exp h - 1}{h} = 1,$$

and, combining this result with the corresponding result when $h \to 0+$, the theorem follows.

5.3. The logarithmic function. Let e denote the number $\exp 1$. From Theorem 40 it is clear that e lies between 2 and 3. Also, from the definition of $\exp x$, we have

$$e = \lim_{n \to \infty} \left(1 + \frac{1}{n}\right)^n.$$

Putting $x = 1$ in the relation $(\exp x)^p = \exp px$, we see that, when p is a positive integer,

$$e^p = \exp p,$$

and we now use this relationship to define what we mean by e^x when x is any real number. We say, in fact, that for any real number x, e^x is defined to be $\exp x$. With this definition, if p/q is rational, with q a positive integer,

$$\left(e^{p/q}\right)^q = \left\{\exp\left(\frac{p}{q}\right)\right\}^q = \exp\left(\frac{pq}{q}\right) = \exp p = e^p,$$

whence $e^{p/q} = \sqrt[q]{(e^p)}$. This definition of e^x when x is any real number thus reduces to the earlier definition of e^x when x is a rational real number. In view of the properties which have been established for the exponential function, we have at once the following results :—

$$e^{x_1}e^{x_2} = e^{x_1+x_2},$$
$$e^0 = 1,$$
$$(e^x)^p = e^{px}, \quad (p \text{ a positive integer})$$

which hold for any real numbers x, x_1 and x_2.

Let $y = e^x$. Since $e^x \to \infty$ as $x \to \infty$ and $e^x \to 0$ as $x \to -\infty$ and since e^x is monotonic strictly increasing and continuous for all values of x, we see by Theorem 35 that there is one value of x corresponding to each positive value of y. Let $x = L(y)$. Then, also by Theorem 35, $L(y)$ is monotonic strictly increasing and continuous for $y > 0$. This function $L(y)$ is usually denoted by $\log y$, or by $\log_e y$, and is called the logarithm of y or the **logarithm** of y to the **base** e. Thus $x = \log(e^x)$, (all values of x). In particular, $\log e = 1$, $y = e^{\log y}$, $(y > 0)$.

The familiar properties of the logarithm now follow immediately. Since $e^0 = 1$ we have $\log 1 = 0$. If $y > 1$ then $x > 0$ so that $\log y > 0$, $(y > 1)$, and similarly $\log y < 0$, $(0 < y < 1)$. Given any positive number K, we have $\log y > K$ whenever $y > e^K$, so that $\log y \to \infty$ as $y \to \infty$. Similarly, $\log y \to -\infty$ as $y \to 0+$.

THEOREM 42. *If y_1, y_2, y are any positive real numbers and p is a positive integer,*

(i) $\log y_1 + \log y_2 = \log y_1 y_2,$

(ii) $\log y_1 - \log y_2 = \log(y_1/y_2),$

(iii) $\log(y^p) = p \log y.$

Let $x_1 = \log y_1$, $x_2 = \log y_2$. Then

$$\log y_1 + \log y_2 = x_1 + x_2 = \log e^{x_1 + x_2}$$
$$= \log e^{x_1} e^{x_2} = \log y_1 y_2,$$

which proves (i). The proof of (ii) is similar.

By mathematical induction we have, for any positive numbers $y_1, y_2, \dots, y_p$,

$$\log y_1 + \log y_2 + \dots + \log y_p = \log(y_1 y_2 \dots y_p),$$

and (iii) follows on writing $y_1 = y_2 = \dots = y_p = y$.

Putting $y_1 = 1$, $y_2 = y$ in (ii) we have, for any positive number y,

$$\log(1/y) = -\log y.$$

Since $y = e^x$ has the non-zero derivative e^x at any point x, it follows by Theorem 36 that the function $\log y$ has derivative $1/e^x$, or $1/y$, for every positive value of y. In particular, since $\log 1 = 0$ and $\log y$ is differentiable at the point 1 with derivative equal to 1, we have

$$\lim_{h \to 0} \frac{\log(1+h)}{h} = 1.$$

5.4. The generalized power. When a is a positive real number we have defined the symbol a^x, so far only in the following cases :—(i) when x is a rational real number, (ii) when a is e and x is any real number. We now extend this definition and state that, *when a is a positive number*, a^x *is to mean* $e^{x \log a}$ *for any real number x*. When $a = e$ this definition reduces to e^x. Also, when x is a rational number of the form p/q, where p, q are integers and q is positive, and if

$$y = a^x = e^{(p/q) \log a},$$

then

$$y^q = \{e^{(p/q) \log a}\}^q = e^{p \log a} = a^p,$$

whence $y = \sqrt[q]{(a^p)}$. The extended definition of a^x thus reduces to the previous definitions of this symbol when

a and x have the appropriate particular sets of values allotted to them.

Clearly a^x is positive for all values of x. It is monotonic strictly increasing for $a > 1$ and tends to infinity as $x \to \infty$. If $0 < a < 1$, it is monotonic strictly decreasing and tends to zero as $x \to \infty$. When $a = 1$, then $a^x = e^0 = 1$. Further, a^x is continuous for all values of x.

It is easy to see that a^x, as defined above, satisfies the laws of indices for, if x_1, x_2 are any real numbers, and a and b are positive,

$$a^{x_1 + x_2} = e^{(x_1 + x_2)\log a} = e^{x_1 \log a + x_2 \log a}$$
$$= e^{x_1 \log a} e^{x_2 \log a} = a^{x_1} a^{x_2},$$
$$\{a^{x_1}\}^{x_2} = e^{x_2 \log (a^{x_1})} = e^{x_2 \log e^{x_1 \log a}}$$
$$= e^{x_2 x_1 \log a} = a^{x_1 x_2},$$
$$\{ab\}^{x_1} = e^{x_1 \log ab} = e^{x_1 \log a + x_1 \log b}$$
$$= e^{x_1 \log a} e^{x_1 \log b} = a^{x_1} b^{x_1}.$$

It has already been shown that $\log(y^p) = p \log y$ for all positive real numbers y and p a positive integer. We may now replace p by any real number x, since

$$\log(y^x) = \log(e^{x \log y}) = x \log y.$$

If $y = a^x$ and $a > 1$, then x is a monotonic increasing function of y for $y > 0$, which tends to infinity as $y \to \infty$, and tends to $-\infty$ as $y \to 0+$. If $0 < a < 1$, we may write $b = 1/a$ and derive at once that, in this case, x is a monotonic decreasing function of y, for $y > 0$, which tends to $-\infty$ as $y \to \infty$ and to $+\infty$ as $y \to 0+$. This function x of y is denoted by $\log_a y$, and is called the **logarithm** of y to the **base** a.

If $x = \log_a y$, then $y = a^x = e^{x \log a}$, whence

$$\log_e y = x \log a = \log_a y \log_e a,$$

which, on transposition gives,

$$\log_a y = \frac{\log_e y}{\log_e a}.$$

Again, if a and b are any positive real numbers,

$$\frac{\log_b y}{\log_a y} = \frac{\log_e y}{\log_e b} \cdot \frac{\log_e a}{\log_e y} = \frac{\log_e a}{\log_e b}$$

$$= \log_b a,$$

which, in the form,

$$\log_a y = \frac{\log_b y}{\log_b a},$$

is the usual change of base formula for logarithms. Putting $y = b$ we have, in particular,

$$\log_a b = 1/\log_b a.$$

In paragraph 3.2. it was pointed out that, in general, it is not possible to infer that a function, which is known to tend to a limit when $n \to \infty$, will also tend to a limit when n is replaced by a variable which tends to infinity through any set of values. It is easy, however, to show that, in the case of the limit

$$e^x = \lim_{n \to \infty} \left(1 + \frac{x}{n}\right)^n,$$

we may replace the positive integer n by any positive number y.

Let n be the integer next smaller than y, if y is not a positive integer, and let n be equal to y, if y is a positive integer. Then $y \to \infty$ as $n \to \infty$, and vice versa. If $x > 0$, we then have

$$\left(1 + \frac{x}{n+1}\right)^n < \left(1 + \frac{x}{y}\right)^y < \left(1 + \frac{x}{n}\right)^{n+1},$$

F

which may be written

$$\frac{\left(1+\dfrac{x}{n+1}\right)^{n+1}}{1+\dfrac{x}{n+1}} < \left(1+\frac{x}{y}\right)^{y} < \left(1+\frac{x}{n}\right)^{n}\left(1+\frac{x}{n}\right).$$

As $y \to \infty$ the expressions on the extreme left and right tend to e^x, by Theorem 37. Thus so also does the expression required. When $x < 0$ the same argument holds, with the inequalities reversed and with y taken to be greater than $|x| + 1$. This restriction on y is merely imposed to ensure that all the terms in the argument are positive.

We conclude this section by noting that the derivative of the function

$$x^{\alpha} = e^{\alpha \log x}, \quad (x > 0, \ \alpha \neq 0)$$

at the point x is

$$\frac{\alpha}{x} e^{\alpha \log x} = \alpha x^{\alpha - 1}.$$

This follows from Theorems 31 and 41.

5.5. The hyperbolic functions.

The hyperbolic functions $\sinh x$, $\cosh x$, $\tanh x$ are defined, for all values of x, as follows:—

$$\sinh x = \tfrac{1}{2}(e^x - e^{-x}), \ \cosh x = \tfrac{1}{2}(e^x + e^{-x}), \ \tanh x = \frac{\sinh x}{\cosh x}.$$

It is easily verified from these definitions that

$$\sinh 0 = 0, \quad \cosh 0 = 1, \quad \tanh 0 = 0,$$

that, for all values of x,

$$\cosh^2 x - \sinh^2 x = 1, \ D \sinh x = \cosh x, \ D \cosh x = \sinh x,$$

$$\sinh(-x) = -\sinh x, \cosh(-x) = \cosh x,$$

and that

$$\sinh x \to \infty, \ \cosh x \to \infty, \ \tanh x \to 1 \text{ as } x \to \infty.$$

Since $\sinh x$, $\cosh x$ are differentiable for all values of x, it follows from Theorem 29 that these functions are continuous for all x. By direct calculation the following relations, valid for any real numbers x and y, may also be established.

$$\sinh (x+y) = \sinh x \cosh y + \cosh x \sinh y,$$
$$\cosh (x+y) = \cosh x \cosh y + \sinh x \sinh y,$$
$$\sinh 2x = 2 \sinh x \cosh x,$$
$$\cosh 2x = \cosh^2 x + \sinh^2 x,$$
$$\sinh x - \sinh y = 2 \cosh \{\tfrac{1}{2}(x+y)\} \sinh \{\tfrac{1}{2}(x-y)\},$$
$$\cosh x - \cosh y = 2 \sinh \{\tfrac{1}{2}(x+y)\} \sinh \{\tfrac{1}{2}(x-y)\}.$$

It is clear from the last two relations that, since $\sinh x > 0$ when $x > 0$,

$$\sinh x > \sinh y \text{ when } x > y,$$
$$\cosh x > \cosh y \text{ when } x > y > 0,$$

from which it follows that $\sinh x$ is monotonic strictly increasing for all values of x and that $\cosh x$ is monotonic strictly increasing for all positive values of x. Also, for all values of x, $\cosh x \geqq 1$.

Other hyperbolic functions which are sometimes used are $\coth x$, $\operatorname{sech} x$, $\operatorname{cosech} x$, and these are defined by the relations

$$\coth x = \frac{1}{\tanh x}, \quad (x \neq 0),$$

$$\operatorname{sech} x = \frac{1}{\cosh x},$$

$$\operatorname{cosech} x = \frac{1}{\sinh x}, \quad (x \neq 0).$$

With these definitions we have

$$D \tanh x = \operatorname{sech}^2 x,$$
$$D \coth x = -\operatorname{cosech}^2 x, \ (x \neq 0),$$
$$D \operatorname{sech} x = -\tanh x \operatorname{sech} x,$$
$$D \operatorname{cosech} x = -\coth x \operatorname{cosech} x, \ (x \neq 0).$$

In short, all the hyperbolic functions are differentiable at all points at which they are defined.

Examples V

(1) If, for $n = 1, 2, \ldots$

$$a_{n+2} = \tfrac{1}{2}(a_n + a_{n+1}),$$

where $a_2 > a_1 > 0$, show that the function a_{2n-1} is monotonic increasing and that a_{2n} is monotonic decreasing. Deduce that a_{2n-1} and a_{2n} have a common limit as $n \to \infty$.

Show that the same result holds if the given relation is replaced by the relation

$$a_{n+2} = \sqrt{(a_n a_{n+1})}, \quad a_2 > a_1 > 0.$$

(2) Evaluate

$$\text{(i)} \ \lim_{x \to 0} \frac{x - \log(1-x)}{2x + \log(1+x)}; \quad \text{(ii)} \ \lim_{x \to 0} \frac{e^x - 1}{\log(1+x)^2};$$

$$\text{(iii)} \ \lim_{x \to 0} \frac{2x^2 - x^3}{\{\log(1+x)\}^2}; \quad \text{(iv)} \ \lim_{x \to 1} \frac{\log x}{x^2 - 1}.$$

(3) Prove that

$$\text{(i)} \ \lim_{n \to \infty} \left(\frac{2n+1}{2n}\right)^n = e^{\frac{1}{2}}; \quad \text{(ii)} \ \lim_{x \to 0} (1-x)^{1/x} = e^{-1};$$

$$\text{(iii)} \ \lim_{x \to \infty} (1 + e^{-x})^{2^x} = 1.$$

(4) If $t = \tanh \dfrac{x}{2}$, prove that

(i) $\tanh x = \dfrac{2t}{1+t^2}$;   (ii) $\sinh x = \dfrac{2t}{1-t^2}$.

(5) Prove that

(i) $\lim\limits_{x \to 0} \dfrac{\sinh x}{x} = 1$;   (ii) $\lim\limits_{x \to 0} \dfrac{\tanh x}{x} = 1$;

(iii) $\lim\limits_{x \to 0} \dfrac{1-\cosh x}{x} = 0$.

(6) If $x = \sinh y$ show that y is a monotonic strictly increasing function of x for all values of x. Prove also, for all values of x,

(i) $\dfrac{dy}{dx} = \dfrac{1}{\sqrt{(1+x^2)}}$;   (ii) $y = \log\{x + \sqrt{(1+x^2)}\}$.

CHAPTER VI

THE TAYLOR EXPANSION

6.1. Further properties of continuous functions. As a preliminary to the discussion of mean value theorems for differentiation, we require two important properties of continuous functions.

THEOREM 43. *If $f(x)$ is continuous in the closed interval $a \leqq x \leqq b$, it is bounded in that interval.*

Suppose that $f(x)$ is not bounded in $a \leqq x \leqq b$. Divide (a, b) into two equal parts. Then, in at least one of these parts, $f(x)$ is not bounded. Denote this part by (a_1, b_1). If $f(x)$ is unbounded in both parts, choose the left hand part and denote it by (a_1, b_1). Now bisect (a_1, b_1) and, by the same construction, obtain a part (a_2, b_2) in which $f(x)$ is unbounded. Continuing in this way, we obtain an interval (a_n, b_n) in which $f(x)$ is unbounded. Clearly

$$a \leqq a_1 \leqq a_2 \leqq \ldots \leqq a_n \leqq \ldots \leqq b,$$
$$b \geqq b_1 \geqq b_2 \geqq \ldots \geqq b_n \geqq \ldots \geqq a,$$

and

$$b_n - a_n = 2^{-n}(b-a).$$

It follows that a_n and b_n have a common limit ξ, say, as $n \to \infty$, where $a \leqq \xi \leqq b$.

Choose any positive number ε. Then, since $f(x)$ is continuous at the point ξ, we can find δ such that

$$f(\xi) - \varepsilon < f(x) < f(\xi) + \varepsilon,$$

for all values of x in (a, b) satisfying the inequalities

$$\xi - \delta < x < \xi + \delta.$$

78

In other words, $f(x)$ is bounded in the open interval $(\xi - \delta, \xi + \delta)$. Since, as $n \to \infty$, a_n and b_n tend to ξ, we can find a value N of n such that

$$\xi - \delta < a_N < b_N < \xi + \delta.$$

The theorem now follows since there is no contradiction involved in the assertion that $f(x)$ is bounded in $(\xi - \delta, \xi + \delta)$ and unbounded in (a_N, b_N).

It should be noted that, in this theorem, the interval of continuity of $f(x)$ must be closed. Thus $1/x$ is continuous for $0 < x \leq 1$, but it is not bounded in this interval.

THEOREM 44. *If $f(x)$ is continuous for $a \leq x \leq b$, its least upper bound is a value of $f(x)$ for some value of x in $a \leq x \leq b$. The same property holds also for the greatest lower bound.*

We shall prove the theorem for the least upper bound, the proof in the case of the greatest lower bound being similar.

By Theorem 43, $f(x)$ has a least upper bound for values of x in $a \leq x \leq b$. Let M be this least upper bound, and suppose that there is no value of x in $a \leq x \leq b$ for which $f(x) = M$. Then $M - f(x)$ is a *positive*, continuous function of x for $a \leq x \leq b$, and so also is $1/\{M - f(x)\}$. This latter function must then have a *positive* least upper bound k, say. It follows that, for all values of x in $a \leq x \leq b$,

$$\frac{1}{M - f(x)} \leq k,$$

and this is the same as saying that, for all x in $a \leq x \leq b$,

$$f(x) \leq M - \frac{1}{k},$$

which contradicts the fact that M is the least upper bound of $f(x)$ for such x.

6.2. The Taylor expansion. The remainder of this chapter deals mainly with methods of obtaining expansions of functions in the form of infinite series and, in particular, with such expansions for the functions which have been defined in the preceding chapters. The expansions are all based on a classical theorem known as Taylor's Theorem, as a preliminary to the proof of which, we require some additional properties of differentiable functions.

THEOREM 45. *If $f(x)$ is differentiable at a point ξ and $f'(\xi) > 0$, there is an interval $(\xi, \xi + \eta)$ to the right of ξ, such that, for all points x within this interval, $f(x) > f(\xi)$; and there is an interval $(\xi - \eta, \xi)$ to the left of ξ, such that, for all points x within this interval, $f(x) < f(\xi)$.*

Choose any ε such that $0 < \varepsilon < f'(\xi)$. Then, since $f(x)$ is differentiable at ξ, we can find η such that

$$0 < f'(\xi) - \varepsilon < \frac{f(\xi + h) - f(\xi)}{h} < f'(\xi) + \varepsilon,$$

whenever $|h| < \eta$. It follows that, when $|h| < \eta$,

$$f(\xi + h) - f(\xi)$$

has the same sign as h. Hence $f(\xi + h) > f(\xi)$ whenever $0 < h < \eta$, and $f(\xi + h) < f(\xi)$ whenever $-\eta < h < 0$. This proves the theorem.

THEOREM 46. **(Rolle's Theorem)**. *If $f(x)$ is differentiable for $a \leqq x \leqq b$, and if $f(a) = f(b) = k$, then there is at least one point ξ, $(a < \xi < b)$, such that $f'(\xi) = 0$.*

If $f(x) = k$ for all x in (a, b), the result follows at once, and ξ may be any point of (a, b).

If $f(x)$ is not equal to k for all x in (a, b), there are values of x in this interval for which the function $\phi(x) = f(x) - k$ takes positive values, or there are values of x for which $\phi(x)$ takes negative values, or $\phi(x)$ may assume positive values and negative values. Suppose that $\phi(x)$ has some positive values. Now $\phi(x)$, being differentiable for $a \leqq x \leqq b$, is also continuous for $a \leqq x \leqq b$ by Theorem 27 and therefore, by Theorem 44, has a least upper bound M, which is a value of $\phi(x)$ for some value ξ of x in $a \leqq x \leqq b$. This least upper bound M is positive, whence ξ can neither be a nor b. We now prove that $\phi'(\xi) = 0$. Suppose if possible that $\phi'(\xi) > 0$. It follows, by Theorem 45, that there is an interval $(\xi, \xi+h)$, to the right of ξ, within which $\phi(x) > \phi(\xi) = M$, which contradicts the definition of M. Similarly if $\phi'(\xi) < 0$, there is an interval $(\xi-h, \xi)$, to the left of ξ, within which $\phi(x) > \phi(\xi) = M$, which contradicts the definition of M. Hence $\phi'(\xi) = 0$, and therefore $f'(\xi) = \phi'(\xi) = 0$. A similar argument holds when $\phi(x)$ has some negative values. The theorem is therefore proved.

With the geometrical interpretation of the value of the derivative of a function at a point as the slope or gradient of the graph of the function at that point, this theorem states that, if the ordinates of the graph of a differentiable function at two points are equal, there is a horizontal tangent to the graph at some point between the two points.

THEOREM 47 (**First Mean Value Theorem**). *If $f(x)$ is differentiable for $a \leqq x \leqq b$, there is a point ξ, $(a < \xi < b)$, for which*

$$f(b) = f(a) + (b-a)f'(\xi).$$

Let

$$Q = \frac{f(b)-f(a)}{b-a}, \quad \phi(x) = f(b)-f(x)-(b-x)Q.$$

Then $\phi(x)$ is differentiable in $a \leqq x \leqq b$, and $\phi(a) = \phi(b) = 0$. Hence, by Theorem 46, $\phi'(x) = 0$ for some value ξ of x such that $a < \xi < b$. But

$$\phi'(x) = -f'(x) + Q,$$

whence $Q = f'(\xi)$, and the result follows. If $b < a$ we obtain the same conclusion with the interval $a < \xi < b$ replaced by $b < \xi < a$.

Geometrically, this theorem means that the gradient of a chord, joining two points on the graph of a differentiable function, is equal to the gradient of a tangent at some point whose abscissa lies between the abscissae of the two points. The next theorem is an immediate deduction from Theorem 47.

THEOREM 48.   *If $f(x)$ is differentiable in an interval (a, b), then $f'(x) > 0$ throughout (a, b) implies that $f(x)$ is monotonic strictly increasing in (a, b). Also $f'(x) < 0$ throughout (a, b) implies that $f(x)$ is monotonic strictly decreasing in (a, b), and $f'(x) = 0$ throughout (a, b) that $f(x)$ is constant in (a, b).*

Let x_1, x_2 be any two points in (a, b) with $x_1 < x_2$. Then, by Theorem 47, there is a number ξ, $(a < \xi < b)$, such that

$$f(x_2) - f(x_1) = (x_2 - x_1)f'(\xi),$$

and the three required results now follow at once, since they correspond to the cases $f'(\xi) > 0$, $f'(\xi) < 0$, $f'(\xi) = 0$.

If $f(x)$ is a differentiable function of x for $a \leq x \leq b$, its derivative $f'(x)$ is a function of x for $a \leq x \leq b$, and it may happen that $f'(x)$ is also differentiable for such x. In this event, the derivative of $f'(x)$ at the point x_0 is denoted by $f''(x_0)$, and $f(x)$ is then said to be twice differentiable at x_0. It will be twice differentiable for $a \leq x \leq b$ if it is twice differentiable at every point of (a, b). We may clearly proceed with further definitions of this kind. Thus $f(x)$ is said to be n times differentiable at x_0 if $f^{(n-1)}(x)$ is differentiable at x_0, where $f^{(n-1)}(x)$ denotes the $(n-1)_{th}$ derivative of $f(x)$ at the point x, and $f(x)$ is said to be n times differentiable for $a \leq x \leq b$ if it is n times differentiable at each point of (a, b). It will be noted from Theorem 27 that, if $f(x)$ is n times differentiable at a point x_0, then the functions $f^{(n-1)}(x)$, $f^{(n-2)}(x)$, ... $f'(x)$, $f(x)$ must all be continuous at x_0.

We proceed to consider Taylor's Theorem which is, in effect, an extension of Theorem 47.

THEOREM 49 (**Taylor's Theorem**). *If $f(x)$ is n times differentiable for $a \leqq x \leqq b$, there is a point ξ ($a < \xi < b$) such that*

$$f(b) = f(a) + \frac{b-a}{1!} f'(a) + \ldots + \frac{(b-a)^{n-1}}{(n-1)!} f^{(n-1)}(a) + R_n,$$

where

$$R_n = \frac{(b-a)^p (b-\xi)^{n-p} f^{(n)}(\xi)}{p(n-1)!},$$

and p is a given number satisfying $p \geqq 1$.

Let Q denote the expression

$$\frac{1}{(b-a)^p} \left\{ f(b) - f(a) - \frac{b-a}{1!} f'(a) - \ldots - \frac{(b-a)^{n-1}}{(n-1)!} f^{(n-1)}(a) \right\},$$

and let

$$\phi(x) = f(b) - f(x) - \frac{b-x}{1!} f'(x) - \ldots$$
$$- \frac{(b-x)^{n-1}}{(n-1)!} f^{(n-1)}(x) - (b-x)^p Q.$$

Then $\phi(x)$ is differentiable for $a \leqq x \leqq b$, since $f(x)$ is n times differentiable for such x. Also $\psi(a) = \phi(b) = 0$. Hence, by Theorem 46, $\phi'(x) = 0$ for some value ζ of x such that $a < \zeta < b$. But

$$\phi'(x) = -f'(x) + \left\{ f'(x) - \frac{b-x}{1!} f''(x) \right\}$$
$$+ \left\{ \frac{b-x}{1!} f''(x) - \frac{(b-x)^2}{2!} f'''(x) \right\}$$
$$+ \left\{ \frac{(b-x)^{n-2}}{(n-2)!} f^{(n-1)}(x) - \frac{(b-x)^{n-1}}{(n-1)!} f^{(n)}(x) \right\}$$
$$+ p(b-x)^{p-1} Q,$$

whence

$$Q = \frac{(b-\xi)^{n-p}}{p(n-1)!} f^{(n)}(\xi),$$

and the result follows. If $b < a$ we obtain the same conclusion with the interval $a < \xi < b$ replaced by $b < \xi < a$.

The expansion occurring in the theorem may be written in different forms. Thus, if we write $h = b - a$, we may express ξ in the form $a + \theta h$, where θ is some number between 0 and 1, and the expansion becomes

$$f(a+h) = f(a) + \frac{h}{1!} f'(a) + \ldots + \frac{h^{n-1}}{(n-1)!} f^{(n-1)}(a)$$

$$+ \frac{h^n}{p(n-1)!} (1-\theta)^{n-p} f^{(n)}(a+\theta h).$$

With a replaced by zero, it becomes

$$f(h) = f(0) + \frac{h}{1!} f'(0) + \ldots + \frac{h^{n-1}}{(n-1)!} f^{(n-1)}(0)$$

$$+ \frac{h^n}{p(n-1)!} (1-\theta)^{n-p} f^{(n)}(\theta h),$$

the expression being valid if $f(x)$ is n times differentiable for $0 \leq x \leq h$. If $h < 0$, $f(x)$ must be n times differentiable for $h \leq x \leq 0$. This last form of the Taylor Expansion is usually called the **Maclaurin Expansion**.

It should be noted that the value of ξ, which occurs in R_n in Theorem 49, will depend in general on the values of a, b, p and n. The same remark applies to θ. The last term in each of these expansions is usually called the **remainder term**. In Maclaurin's form this remainder term is given by

$$R_n = \frac{h^n}{p(n-1)!} (1-\theta)^{n-p} f^{(n)}(\theta h),$$

where the integer p is at our disposal and $0 < \theta < 1$. When $p = n$, we have

$$R_n = \frac{h^n}{n!} f^{(n)}(\theta h),$$

and this is called **Lagrange's form of the remainder term**. When $p = 1$, we have

$$R_n = \frac{h^n}{(n-1)!} (1-\theta)^{n-1} f^{(n)}(\theta h),$$

and this is called **Cauchy's form of the remainder term**.

Essentially, the importance of Taylor's Theorem lies in the fact that it relates the values of a function and its first $(n-1)$ derivatives at one point a to its approximate value at another point b, where both a and b lie in an interval in which the function is n times differentiable.

We now apply Taylor's Theorem to functions which have been defined in earlier chapters. We shall in fact use the Maclaurin form with h replaced by x. The validity of the expansion, it must be remembered, extends to those values of x in an interval surrounding the point zero within which the function concerned is n times differentiable.

THEOREM 50. *If x is any real number, we have*

(i) $e^x = 1 + \dfrac{x}{1!} + \dfrac{x^2}{2!} + \ldots + \dfrac{x^{n-1}}{(n-1)!} e^{\theta x},$

(ii) $\sinh x = x + \dfrac{x^3}{3!} + \ldots + \dfrac{x^{2n-1}}{(2n-1)!} + \dfrac{x^{2n}}{(2n)!} \sinh(\theta x),$

(iii) $\cosh x = 1 + \dfrac{x^2}{2!} + \ldots + \dfrac{x^{2n}}{(2n)!} + \dfrac{x^{2n+1}}{(2n+1)!} \sinh(\theta x),$

and, if x is any real number greater than -1,

(iv) $\log(1+x) = x - \dfrac{x^2}{2} + \dfrac{x^3}{3} - \ldots + (-1)^{n-2} \dfrac{x^{n-1}}{n-1}$

$$+ \frac{(-1)^{n-1}}{n} \frac{x^n}{(1+\theta x)^n},$$

or

$$\log(1+x) = x - \frac{x^2}{2} + \frac{x^3}{3} - \ldots + (-1)^{n-2}\frac{x^{n-1}}{n-1}$$
$$+ (-1)^{n-1}(1-\theta)^{n-1}\frac{x^n}{(1+\theta x)^n},$$

(v) $$(1+x)^\alpha = 1 + \binom{\alpha}{1}x + \ldots + \binom{\alpha}{n-1}x^{n-1}$$
$$+ \frac{\alpha(\alpha-1)\ldots(\alpha-n+1)}{(n-1)!}\frac{(1-\theta)^{n-1}}{(1+\theta x)^{n-\alpha}}x^n,$$

where α is any real number except a positive integer. The numbers θ all satisfy the relation $0 < \theta < 1$, but do not necessarily have the same value each time they occur.

The proof of (i) is immediate since, for every positive integer r,

$$\frac{d^r}{dx^r}e^x\bigg]_{x=0} = 1.$$

In the case of (ii), when r is odd,

$$\frac{d^r}{dx^r}\sinh x = \cosh x = 1,$$

when $x = 0$, and, when r is even,

$$\frac{d^r}{dx^r}\sinh x = \sinh x = 0,$$

when $x = 0$, and the result follows from Taylor's Theorem on taking $2n$ terms instead of n.

The deduction of (iii) is similar since, when r is odd,

$$\frac{d^r}{dx^r}\cosh x = \sinh x = 0,$$

when $x = 0$, and, when r is even,

$$\frac{d^r}{dx^r} \cosh x = \cosh x = 1,$$

when $x = 0$. In this case we employ $2n+1$ terms.

To deduce (iv), we have seen that $\log(1+x)$ is differentiable for $x > -1$ and that, for such x,

$$D \log(1+x) = \frac{1}{1+x}.$$

It is now clear that $\log(1+x)$ is differentiable, for $x > -1$, as many times as we please and that

$$D^n \log(1+x) = \frac{(-1)^{n-1}(n-1)!}{(1+x)^n}.$$

Thus

$$D^n \log(1+x)\Big]_{x=0} = (-1)^{n-1}(n-1)!.$$

Hence, by Taylor's Theorem, for $x > -1$,

$$\log(1+x) = \sum_{r=1}^{n-1} \frac{(-1)^{r-1}(r-1)!}{r!} x^r$$
$$+ \frac{(-1)^{n-1}(n-1)!}{n!} \frac{x^n}{(1+\theta x)^n},$$

which is the first result required. The second follows in the same way except that it involves the Cauchy instead of the Lagrange form of remainder.

In the case of (v), we have, for $x > -1$, if α is not a positive integer,

$$(1+x)^\alpha = e^{\alpha \log(1+x)},$$

and

$$D\{(1+x)^\alpha\} = e^{\alpha \log(1+x)} \frac{\alpha}{1+x} = \alpha(1+x)^{\alpha-1} = \alpha,$$

when $x = 0$. Clearly $(1+x)^\alpha$ is differentiable for $x > -1$ as many times as we please and

$$D^n\{(1+x)^\alpha\} = \alpha(\alpha-1)\ldots(\alpha-n+1)(1+x)^{\alpha-n}$$
$$= \alpha(\alpha-1)\ldots(\alpha-n+1),$$

when $x = 0$. Hence, for $x > -1$, we have

$$(1+x)^\alpha = 1 + \frac{\alpha}{1}x + \frac{\alpha(\alpha-1)}{1.2}x^2 + \ldots + \frac{\alpha(\alpha-1)\ldots(\alpha-n+2)}{1.2\ldots(n-1)}x^{n-1}$$
$$+ \frac{\alpha(\alpha-1)\ldots(\alpha-n+1)}{1.2\ldots(n-1)}\frac{(1-\theta)^{n-1}}{(1+\theta x)^{n-\alpha}}x^n,$$

if we use the Cauchy rather than the Lagrange form of remainder.

It will be noted that in (v), when α is a positive integer, the left hand side is simply $1+x$ multiplied by itself α times, and we have the ordinary straightforward case of the Binomial Theorem.

6.3. Infinite series. Suppose that a_n is a function of n, defined for all positive integral values of n, and that

$$A_n = a_1 + a_2 + \ldots + a_n.$$

Then A_n is also defined for such n and may or may not have a limit as $n \to \infty$. If it does have a finite limit s, we say that the series $a_1 + a_2 + \ldots$ is convergent and has sum s, and we write

$$\sum_{n=1}^{\infty} a_n = s.$$

If A_n does not have a finite limit as $n \to \infty$, we say that the series $a_1 + a_2 + \ldots$ is divergent.

Thus, to say that a series $a_1 + a_2 + \ldots$ is convergent to a certain sum s is the same as saying that $a_1 + a_2 + \ldots + a_n$ tends to s as $n \to \infty$. For example, the series $1 + 0 + 0 + 0 \ldots$ is convergent to the sum 1, since, in the notation above, $A_n = 1$ for every positive integer n, and therefore tends to 1 as $n \to \infty$.

Instead of writing out a series $a_1 + a_2 + \ldots$ in this extended form we often write it, whether convergent or not, in the form $\sum_{n=1}^{\infty} a_n$.

THEOREM 51. *If the series*

$$\sum_{n=1}^{\infty} a_n, \quad \sum_{n=1}^{\infty} b_n$$

are convergent to the sums s and t respectively, and if α and β are any real numbers independent of n, then the series

$$\sum_{n=1}^{\infty} (\alpha a_n + \beta b_n)$$

is convergent to the sum $\alpha s + \beta t$.

Let

$$A_n = \sum_{r=1}^{n} a_r, \quad B_n = \sum_{r=1}^{n} b_r, \quad C_n = \sum_{r=1}^{n} (\alpha a_r + \beta b_r).$$

We have to prove that $C_n \to \alpha s + \beta t$ as $n \to \infty$. Clearly, for each positive integral value of n,

$$C_n = \alpha A_n + \beta B_n \to \alpha s + \beta t,$$

as $n \to \infty$ by hypothesis.

It follows at once from this theorem that, if a series $a_1 + a_2 + \ldots$ converges to a sum s, the series $a_2 + a_3 + \ldots$ will converge to the sum $s - a_1$, since the second series is obtained from the first by subtracting from each term the corresponding term of the series $a_1 + 0 + 0 + \ldots$. In a similar way, we see that it is possible to add a new term at the beginning of a convergent series and alter the sum in the expected way.

We are now in a position to obtain expansions in the form of infinite series of the functions considered in Theorem 50.

G

THEOREM 52.   *For all values of x, we have*

(i) $e^x = \sum_{n=0}^{\infty} \dfrac{x^n}{n!} = 1 + \dfrac{x}{1!} + \dfrac{x^2}{2!} + \ldots$

(ii) $\sinh x = \sum_{n=1}^{\infty} \dfrac{x^{2n-1}}{(2n-1)!} = x + \dfrac{x^3}{3!} + \dfrac{x^5}{5!} + \ldots$

(iii) $\cosh x = \sum_{n=0}^{\infty} \dfrac{x^{2n}}{(2n)!} = 1 + \dfrac{x^2}{2!} + \dfrac{x^4}{4!} + \ldots;$

for all values of x satisfying $-1 < x \leqq 1$, *we have*

(iv) $\log(1+x) = \sum_{n=1}^{\infty} \dfrac{(-1)^{n-1}x^n}{n} = x - \dfrac{x^2}{2} + \dfrac{x^3}{3} - \ldots,$

and for all values of x satisfying $-1 < x < 1$, *we have*

(v) $(1+x)^\alpha = \sum_{n=0}^{\infty} \binom{\alpha}{n} x^n = 1 + \binom{\alpha}{1} x + \binom{\alpha}{2} x^2 + \ldots,$

where α *is any real number except a positive integer.*

We have to show that, in each case, the series on the right converges for the appropriate values of x, and that the sum is the expression on the left. We shall use A_n to denote the sum of the first n terms in each case.

(i) Let x be any real number. Then, from Theorem 50,

$$\left| A_n - e^x \right| = \left| \dfrac{x^n}{n!} e^{\theta x} \right| \leqq e^{\theta |x|} \dfrac{|x|^n}{n!} < e^{|x|} \dfrac{|x|^n}{n!},$$

and the result will be established if we show that $|x|^n/n! \to 0$ as $n \to \infty$. Let p be the integer next above $|x|$, if $|x|$ is not an integer, and equal to $|x|$, if $|x|$ is an integer. Then, for $n > p$,

$$0 \leqq \dfrac{|x|^n}{n!} \leqq \dfrac{p^p}{p!} \cdot \dfrac{p^{n-p}}{(p+1)\ldots n} < \dfrac{p^p}{p!}\left(\dfrac{p}{p+1}\right)^{n-p} = \dfrac{(p+1)^p}{p!}\left(\dfrac{p}{p+1}\right)^n,$$

which tends to zero as $n \to \infty$ since $0 < p/(p+1) < 1$. The result follows.

(ii) Let x be any real number. Then, from Theorem 50,

$$\left| A_n - \sinh x \right| = \left| \frac{x^{2n}}{(2n)!} \sinh(\theta x) \right| \le \sinh(\theta |x|) \frac{|x|^{2n}}{(2n)!}$$
$$\le \sinh |x| \cdot \frac{|x|^{2n}}{(2n)!},$$

and this tends to zero as $n \to \infty$, by the argument in (i).

(iii) This follows similarly, since, in this case

$$\left| A_{n+1} - \cosh x \right| = \left| \sinh(\theta x) \frac{x^{2n+1}}{(2n+1)!} \right|,$$

which tends to zero as $n \to \infty$. Thus $A_{n+1} \to \cosh x$, and therefore $A_n \to \cosh x$.

(iv) We note first that, if $x = 0$, the result is immediate. If $0 < x \le 1$ we have, from Theorem 50,

$$\left| A_{n-1} - \log(1+x) \right| = \left| \frac{x^n}{n(1+\theta x)^n} \right| \le \frac{|x|^n}{n} \to 0.$$

Suppose now that δ is any fixed positive number less than unity and that $-1 < -1 + \delta \le x < 0$. Then, from Theorem 50,

$$\left| A_{n-1} - \log(1+x) \right| = \left| \frac{(1-\theta)^{n-1}}{(1+\theta x)^n} x^n \right|$$
$$\le \frac{(1-\theta)^{n-1}}{(1-\theta)^{n-1}} \frac{1}{1+\theta x} |x|^n$$
$$\le \frac{1}{1+x} |x|^n$$
$$\le \frac{1}{\delta} |x|^n \to 0,$$

as $n \to \infty$. Thus, for $-1 < -1 + \delta \leqq x \leqq 1$, A_{n-1} and therefore A_n tends to $\log(1+x)$ as $n \to \infty$. Since δ may be chosen to be as small as we please, it follows that the expansion holds for $-1 < x \leqq 1$.

(v) In this case we have, from Theorem 50, when $x > -1$,

$$\left| A_n - (1+x)^{\alpha} \right| = \left| \frac{\alpha(\alpha-1)\ldots(\alpha-n+1)}{(n-1)!} \frac{(1-\theta)^{n-1}}{(1+\theta x)^{n-\alpha}} x^n \right|$$

$$= \frac{(1-\theta)^{n-1}}{(1+\theta x)^{n-1}} (1+\theta x)^{\alpha-1} K_n \left| x^n \right|,$$

say, where

$$K_n = \left| \frac{\alpha(\alpha-1)\ldots(\alpha-n+1)}{1.2\ldots(n-1)} \right|.$$

We proceed to show that $K_n < A n^{q+1}$, where A and q are some numbers independent of n. Throughout the proof we shall use A in this sense, on the understanding that it need not have the same value on each occasion when it occurs. Suppose first that α is positive, but not an integer. Let p be the integer next below α. Then, for $n > p+1$,

$$K_n = \left\{ \frac{\alpha(\alpha-1)\ldots(\alpha-p)}{1.2\ldots p} \right\} \left\{ \frac{(p+1-\alpha)(p+2-\alpha)\ldots(n-1-\alpha)}{(p+1)(p+2)\ldots(n-1)} \right\}$$

$$< A \left(1 - \frac{\alpha}{p+1}\right) \left(1 - \frac{\alpha}{p+2}\right) \ldots \left(1 - \frac{\alpha}{n-1}\right).$$

and, since each factor lies between 0 and 1, we have $K_n < A$, for all $n > p+1$. Suppose now that α is negative. Let $\beta = -\alpha$, so that $\beta > 0$. Then, if q is the integer next below β, if β is not an integer, and equal to β, if β is an integer, and if $n > q$,

$$K_n = \frac{\beta(\beta+1)\ldots(\beta+n-1)}{1.2\ldots(n-1)}$$

$$= \left\{\frac{(\beta+n-1)(\beta+n-2)\ldots(\beta+n-q-1)}{1.2\ldots q}\right\} \times$$

$$\left\{\frac{(\beta+n-q-2)(\beta+n-q-3)\ldots(\beta+1)\beta}{(n-1)(n-2)\ldots(q+1)}\right\}$$

$$= \left\{\frac{(\beta+n-1)(\beta+n-2)\ldots(\beta+n-q-1)}{q!}\right\} \times$$

$$\left\{\left(1-\frac{q+1-\beta}{n-1}\right)\left(1-\frac{q+1-\beta}{n-2}\right)\ldots\left(1-\frac{q+1-\beta}{q+1}\right)\right\}.$$

Since each factor in the second bracket lies between 0 and 1, and $\beta \leq n$,

$$K_n \leq \frac{1}{q!}(2n)^{q+1} < An^{q+1}.$$

Hence, for all values of n greater than some fixed integer, whether α be positive or negative,

$$K_n < An^{q+1}.$$

Suppose now that δ is any fixed positive number (< 1), and that x is such that $-1 < -1+\delta \leq x < 1$. Then, from Chapter III, Example 5, $K_n x^n \to 0$ as $n \to \infty$. Also, for every positive integer n,

$$0 < \frac{(1-\theta)^{n-1}}{(1+\theta x)^{n-1}} < \left(\frac{1-\theta}{1-\theta}\right)^{n-1} = 1.$$

Finally, if $0 \leq x < 1$, $1 \leq 1+\theta x < 2$ and, if $-1 < -1+\delta \leq x < 0$, then $\delta \leq 1+x < 1+\theta x < 1$, so that $(1+\theta x)^{\alpha-1}$ is bounded for all positive integers n.

It now follows that $A_n \to (1+x)^{\alpha}$ as $n \to \infty$, whenever $-1 < -1+\delta \leq x < 1$ and, since δ may be chosen to be as small as we please, the expansion is valid for $-1 < x < 1$.

It will be noted that, in the particular case when $x = 1$, it follows from (iv) that the series $1 - \frac{1}{2} + \frac{1}{3} - \ldots$ is convergent and has sum $\log 2$. Also, from (i), the series

$$1 + \frac{1}{1!} + \frac{1}{2!} + \ldots$$

is convergent to the sum e, and this formula provides a convenient means of obtaining approximations to the value of e. Thus, to five places of decimals, $e = 2.71828$.

Examples VI

(1) Show that, for $0 \leqq x \leqq 1$,

$$x - \tfrac{1}{2}x^2 < \log(1+x) < x - \frac{x^2}{2(1+x)^2}.$$

Hence calculate $\log(1.01)$, correct to 5 places of decimals.

(2) Show that, for $x \geqq 0$,

$$1 + x + \frac{x^2}{2} < e^x < \frac{1 + x + \dfrac{x^2}{2}}{1 - \dfrac{x^3}{6}},$$

and hence calculate $e^{0.1}$, correct to three places of decimals.

(3) The functions

$$\frac{1}{x}, \quad \frac{1}{\log(1+x)}, \quad \frac{1}{\sinh x}$$

are continuous for $0 < x \leqq 1$, but they are not bounded in this interval. Explain with reference to Theorem 43.

(4) Determine the least upper and greatest lower bounds of the function

$$y = \frac{x^2}{1+x}, \quad (-\tfrac{1}{2} \leqq x \leqq \tfrac{1}{2}),$$

and verify that they are values of the function in this range of values of x.

(5) If $f(x)$ is defined as follows

$$f(0) = f(1) = \tfrac{1}{2},$$
$$f(x) = x^2, \quad (0 < x < 1),$$

show that the greatest lower and least upper bounds of $f(x)$ are not values of $f(x)$ for $0 \le x \le 1$.

(6) Prove that, for $-1 < x < 1$,

$$\tfrac{1}{2} \log \frac{1+x}{1-x} = x + \frac{x^3}{3} + \frac{x^5}{5} + \dots.$$

(7) Evaluate the following limits:

(i) $\lim\limits_{x \to 0} \dfrac{x \sinh x + 2 - 2 \cosh x}{\{\log(1+x)\}^3}$;

(ii) $\lim\limits_{x \to 0} \dfrac{\sqrt{(1+2x)} - 1 - x}{\sinh^2 x}$;

(iii) $\lim\limits_{x \to 0} \dfrac{(1+x)^\alpha - 1}{(1-x)^\beta - 1}$.

(8) Prove that, for all values of x,

(i) $2e^x \sinh x = \dfrac{(2x)}{1!} + \dfrac{(2x)^2}{2!} + \dots + \dfrac{(2x)^n}{n!} + \dots.$

(ii) $(1+x)e^x = 1 + \dfrac{2x}{1!} + \dfrac{3x^2}{2!} + \dots + \dfrac{(n+1)x^n}{n!} + \dots.$

(9) Show that the conclusions of Theorems 46 and 47 remain valid with the hypotheses, that $f(x)$ is differentiable for $a < x < b$ and $f(x)$ is continuous on the right at a and on the left at b.

CHAPTER VII

THE EVALUATION OF LIMITS

7.1. Standard limits. In this chapter methods of evaluating limits will be discussed. The most effective method is to make use of the fundamental limit theorems given in Chapter 3, together with certain known standard limits. Some standard limits are listed below.

$$\left.\begin{array}{l} x^{\alpha} \to \infty \text{ as } x \to \infty \quad (\alpha > 0) \\ x^{\alpha} \to 0 \text{ as } x \to \infty \quad (\alpha < 0) \end{array}\right\}, \tag{1}$$

$$\left.\begin{array}{l} n^{\alpha} r^{n} \to \infty \text{ as } n \to \infty \quad (r > 1) \\ n^{\alpha} r^{n} \to 0 \text{ as } n \to \infty \quad (-1 < r < 1) \end{array}\right\}. \tag{2}$$

These limits were derived in Chapter 3 on the supposition that α was rational. The extensions to the cases when α is not rational are immediate. For example, in the case of (2) when $-1 < r < 1$, if α is not rational, it is possible to choose a rational ρ, say, such that $\rho > \alpha$. Then

$$\left| n^{\alpha} r^{n} \right| < \left| n^{\rho} r^{n} \right| \to 0 \text{ as } n \to \infty.$$

Further standard limits are

$$\left(1 + \frac{x}{n}\right)^{n} \to e^{x} \text{ as } n \to \infty, \tag{3}$$

$$\frac{\log(1+x)}{x} \to 1 \text{ as } x \to 0, \tag{4}$$

$$\frac{e^{x} - 1}{x} \to 1 \text{ as } x \to 0, \tag{5}$$

$$\frac{\sinh x}{x} \to 1 \text{ as } x \to 0, \tag{6}$$

$$\frac{\cosh x - 1}{x^2} \to \tfrac{1}{2} \text{ as } x \to 0, \tag{7}$$

the last two on the list being easily derived from Theorem 50. From the same theorem it is clear that, if β is any positive real number, there is a positive number K, independent of x, such that, for $x > 1$, $e^x > Kx^\beta$. It follows at once from this that, if α is any real number

$$x^{-\alpha}e^x \to \infty \text{ as } x \to \infty, \tag{8}$$

for, if β be any number greater than α, then

$$x^{-\alpha}e^x > Kx^{\beta-\alpha} \to \infty \text{ as } x \to \infty.$$

It also follows that, if δ is any positive number however small,

$$x^{-\delta} \log x \to 0 \text{ as } x \to \infty, \tag{9}$$

for, writing $y = \delta \log x$, so that $y \to \infty$ as $x \to \infty$,

$$x^{-\delta} \log x = \frac{y}{\delta} e^{-y},$$

which tends to zero as $y \to \infty$ by reciprocating the limit in (8).

Relation (8) shows that, when $x \to \infty$, a power of x is of little importance relative to the exponential function of x, in the sense that the behaviour of the product is exactly the same as the behaviour of the exponential itself. Even although $x^{-\alpha}$ may tend to zero strongly, which will happen when α is large, the product $x^{-\alpha}e^x$ none the less tends to infinity. Relation (9) shows that, when $x \to \infty$, a power of x, however small and positive the index of that power may be, is of very great importance relative to $\log x$. The behaviour of the quotient $\log x/x^\delta$ as $x \to \infty$ is exactly the same as that of $1/x^\delta$, even although $\log x \to \infty$ as $x \to \infty$.

The following examples illustrate the techniques which may be adopted in evaluation:—

Example. Evaluate the limits:—

(i) $\displaystyle\lim_{x\to 0} \frac{\sinh^2 2x}{\log(1+x^2)}$,

(ii) $\displaystyle\lim_{x\to \infty} x^2(e^{(1/x)}-1)\{\log(x+2)-\log x\}$,

(iii) $\displaystyle\lim_{x\to \infty} \frac{x^\alpha}{\log x}\{\log(x+1)\}^2$.

For the sake of brevity we shall denote by $E(x)$ the expressions for which limits have to be found.

For (i), we have

$$E(x) = \left(\frac{\sinh 2x}{2x}\right)^2 . 4 . \frac{x^2}{\log(1+x^2)} \to 1^2 . 4 . 1,$$

as $x\to 0$, by (4), (6) and the analogue for $x\to 0$ of Theorem 17.

In the case of (ii), we have

$$E(x) = x^2 \left(\frac{e^{(1/x)}-1}{\dfrac{1}{x}}\right) \frac{\log\left(1+\dfrac{2}{x}\right)}{\dfrac{2}{x}} . \frac{2}{x^2} \to 1 . 1 . 2,$$

as $x\to \infty$, by (5), (4) and Theorem 17.

In the case of (iii),

$$E(x) = x^\alpha \log x \left\{\frac{\log(x+1)}{\log x}\right\}^2$$

$$= x^\alpha \log x \left\{\frac{\log x + \log\left(1+\dfrac{1}{x}\right)}{\log x}\right\}^2$$

$$= x^\alpha \log x \left\{1 + \frac{1}{\log x} . \log\left(1+\frac{1}{x}\right)\right\}^2.$$

The expression in brackets tends to 1 as $x \to \infty$, so that $E(x) \to \infty$ as $x \to \infty$ if $\alpha \geqq 0$, and to 0 as $x \to \infty$ if $\alpha < 0$.

Certain limits may also be evaluated by making use of the Taylor Expansions given in Theorem 50.

Example. Evaluate

$$\lim_{x \to 0} \frac{2 \cosh x - 2 - x^2}{\{\log(1 + x^2)\}^2}.$$

From Theorem 50,

$$2 \cosh x - 2 - x^2 = 2 \left\{ \frac{x^4}{4!} + \frac{x^5}{5!} \sinh(\theta_1 x) \right\}$$

$$\{\log(1 + x^2)\}^2 = \left\{ x^2 - \frac{x^4}{2} \frac{1}{(1 + \theta_2 x^2)^2} \right\}^2$$

where $0 < \theta_1 < 1$, $0 < \theta_2 < 1$, and, on cancelling x^4, the quotient may be written

$$\frac{\dfrac{1}{12}\left(1 + \dfrac{x}{5} \sinh(\theta_1 x)\right)}{\left\{1 - \dfrac{x^2}{2(1 + \theta_2 x^2)^2}\right\}^2},$$

and, since each expression in brackets tends to 1 as $x \to 0$, the given expression tends to 1/12.

7.2. L'Hôpital's method. Before dealing with this method, we shall derive an extension, which is due to Cauchy, of the Mean Value Theorem. We have seen that if $f(x)$ and $g(x)$ are differentiable for $a \leqq x \leqq b$, then

$$f(b) - f(a) = (b - a)f'(\xi_1),$$
$$g(b) - g(a) = (b - a)g'(\xi_2),$$

where $a < \xi_1 < b$, $a < \xi_2 < b$. It follows that, if $g'(x) \neq 0$ for $a < x < b$, and $g(b) \neq g(a)$, then

$$\frac{f(b) - f(a)}{g(b) - g(a)} = \frac{f'(\xi_1)}{g'(\xi_2)}.$$

The same relation is true with the single condition $g'(x) \neq 0$, $(a \leq x \leq b)$. This condition implies that $g(a) \neq g(b)$, for if $g(a) = g(b)$, there is, by Rolle's Theorem, a point x_0, $(a < x_0 < b)$, at which $g'(x_0) = 0$. Cauchy's modification of the mean value theorem enables us to replace the numbers ξ_1, ξ_2, which are in general different, by a single number ξ.

THEOREM 53. *If $f(x)$ and $g(x)$ are differentiable for $a \leq x \leq b$, and if $g'(x) \neq 0$ for $a \leq x \leq b$, then there is a point ξ ($a < \xi < b$) such that*

$$\frac{f(b)-f(a)}{g(b)-g(a)} = \frac{f'(\xi)}{g'(\xi)}.$$

Let

$$Q = \frac{f(b)-f(a)}{g(b)-g(a)},$$

and let

$$\phi(x) = \{f(x)-f(a)\} - Q\{g(x)-g(a)\}.$$

Then $\phi(x)$ is differentiable for $a \leq x \leq b$, $\phi(a) = \phi(b) = 0$, and therefore, by Rolle's Theorem, there is a point ξ, $(a < \xi < b)$, such that $\phi'(\xi) = 0$. But

$$\phi'(\xi) = f'(\xi) - Qg'(\xi),$$

and the result follows. If $b < a$, we obtain the same conclusion with the interval $a < \xi < b$ replaced by the interval $b < \xi < a$.

THEOREM 54. (**L'Hôpital's Theorem**). *If $f(x)$ and $g(x)$ are differentiable in an interval which includes the point a, if $g'(x)$ is not zero in this interval, except at the point a, and if $f(a) = g(a) = 0$, then the relation*

$$\lim_{x \to a} \frac{f'(x)}{g'(x)} = l$$

implies that

$$\lim_{x \to a} \frac{f(x)}{g(x)} = l.$$

Suppose that x, ($> a$), is any point in the given interval. Then, by Theorem 55, there is a point ξ satisfying $a < \xi < x$, such that

$$\frac{f(x) - f(a)}{g(x) - g(a)} = \frac{f(x)}{g(x)} = \frac{f'(\xi)}{g'(\xi)}.$$

Let $x \to a+$. Then $\xi \to a+$ and

$$\lim_{x \to a+} \frac{f(x)}{g(x)} = l.$$

Similarly

$$\lim_{x \to a-} \frac{f(x)}{g(x)} = l,$$

and the result follows.

There are modifications of this theorem in regard to the conditions imposed on the functions, and also to take into account the case when $f(x)$ and $g(x)$ both tend to infinity as $x \to a$, but the theorem as stated is sufficient to deal with most practical requirements.

Example. Evaluate

$$\lim_{x \to 0} \frac{x \sinh x - 2 + 2 \cosh x}{x^4 + 2x^2}.$$

In the notation of the theorem,

$$\begin{aligned}
f(x) &= x \sinh x - 2 + 2 \cosh x, \\
f'(x) &= 3 \sinh x + x \cosh x, \\
f''(x) &= 4 \cosh x + x \sinh x, \\
g(x) &= x^4 + 2x^2, \\
g'(x) &= 4x^3 + 4x, \\
g''(x) &= 12x^2 + 4.
\end{aligned}$$

By the continuity of the hyperbolic functions,

$$f''(x)/g''(x) \to 1$$

as $x \to 0$. Also there is an interval surrounding $x = 0$, within which neither $g'(x)$ nor $g''(x)$ vanish, except that $g'(0) = 0$. Also $f'(0) = 0$. Hence

$$\lim_{x \to 0} \frac{f'(x)}{g'(x)} = 1.$$

There is an interval surrounding $x = 0$, within which neither $g(x)$ nor $g'(x)$ vanish, except that $g(0) = g'(0) = 0$. Also $f(0) = 0$. Hence

$$\lim_{x \to 0} \frac{f(x)}{g(x)} = 1.$$

The argument may be shortened by making use of the theorem once instead of twice. Thus

$$\frac{f'(x)}{g'(x)} = \frac{3\left(\dfrac{\sinh x}{x}\right) + \cosh x}{4x^2 + 4} \to \frac{4}{4} = 1,$$

as $x \to 0$.

7.3. Stolz's theorem. The method of 7.2 is applicable to cases when x approaches its limiting value a through all values in the neighbourhood of a. This section is devoted to a discussion of the analogue of Theorem 54 for the case of the positive integral variable.

We require a preliminary theorem.

THEOREM 55. *If a_n and b_n are defined for all positive integral values of n, if b_n is positive for such n, and if $B_n = (b_1 + b_2 + \ldots + b_n) \to \infty$ as $n \to \infty$, then the relation*

$$\lim_{n \to \infty} \frac{a_n}{b_n} = l$$

implies that

$$\lim_{n \to \infty} \frac{a_1 + a_2 + \ldots + a_n}{b_1 + b_2 + \ldots + b_n} = l.$$

Let $\alpha_n = a_n - lb_n$, so that

$$\frac{\alpha_n}{b_n} = \frac{a_n}{b_n} - l,$$

and

$$\frac{\alpha_1 + \alpha_2 + \ldots + \alpha_n}{b_1 + b_2 + \ldots + b_n} = \frac{a_1 + a_2 + \ldots + a_n}{b_1 + b_2 + \ldots + b_n} - l.$$

Hence, with the hypothesis on b_n, it is sufficient to show that the relation $\alpha_n/b_n \to 0$ implies the relation

$$\frac{\alpha_1 + \alpha_2 + \ldots + \alpha_n}{b_1 + b_2 + \ldots + b_n} \to 0.$$

Since $\alpha_n/b_n \to 0$, given ε, we can find a positive integer N, such that $|\alpha_n|/b_n < \frac{1}{2}\varepsilon$ whenever $n > N$. We then have, for $n > N$,

$$\frac{|\alpha_1 + \alpha_2 + \ldots + \alpha_n|}{b_1 + b_2 + \ldots + b_n}$$

$$\leqq \frac{|\alpha_1 + \alpha_2 + \ldots + \alpha_N|}{B_n} + \frac{|\alpha_{N+1}| + |\alpha_{N+2}| + \ldots + |\alpha_n|}{B_n}$$

$$< \frac{|\alpha_1 + \alpha_2 + \ldots + \alpha_N|}{B_n} + \frac{1}{2}\varepsilon \frac{b_{N+1} + b_{N+2} + \ldots + b_n}{B_n}$$

$$\leqq \frac{K}{B_n} + \frac{1}{2}\varepsilon,$$

where $K = |\alpha_1 + \alpha_2 + \ldots + \alpha_N|$. Since K is fixed and $B_n \to \infty$ as $n \to \infty$, we can find N_1, such that $B_n > 2K/\varepsilon$ for $n > N_1$. Hence, if $n > \max(N, N_1)$, we have

$$\frac{|\alpha_1 + \alpha_2 + \ldots + \alpha_n|}{B_n} < \varepsilon,$$

from which it follows that, as $n \to \infty$,

$$\frac{\alpha_1 + \alpha_2 + \ldots + \alpha_n}{b_1 + b_2 + \ldots + b_n} \to 0.$$

THEOREM 56 (**Stolz's Theorem**). *If a_n and b_n are defined for all positive integral values of n, if b_n is positive and monotonic strictly increasing for such n, and if $b_n \to \infty$ as $n \to \infty$, then the relation*

$$\lim_{n \to \infty} \frac{a_{n+1} - a_n}{b_{n+1} - b_n} = l$$

implies that

$$\lim_{n \to \infty} \frac{a_n}{b_n} = l.$$

This is an immediate consequence of Theorem 55. For, let $\alpha_1 = a_1$, $\alpha_n = a_n - a_{n-1}$, $(n = 2, 3, \ldots)$, and let $\beta_1 = b_1$, $\beta_n = b_n - b_{n-1}$ $(n = 2, 3, \ldots)$. Then β_n is positive for each n, and

$$\begin{aligned} \beta_1 + \beta_2 + \ldots + \beta_n &= b_1 + (b_2 - b_1) + \ldots + (b_n - b_{n-1}) \\ &= b_n \to \infty, \end{aligned}$$

as $n \to \infty$. Further, the relation

$$\frac{a_{n+1} - a_n}{b_{n+1} - b_n} \to l$$

is the same as the relation

$$\frac{\alpha_{n+1}}{\beta_{n+1}} \to l.$$

It now follows, from Theorem 55, that

$$\frac{\alpha_1 + \alpha_2 + \ldots + \alpha_n}{\beta_1 + \beta_2 + \ldots + \beta_n} \to l,$$

as $n \to \infty$, and this is the same as saying that $a_n / b_n \to l$ as $n \to \infty$.

Example. Evaluate

$$\lim_{n \to \infty} \frac{\sum_{r=1}^{n} \sinh\left(\dfrac{\theta}{\sqrt{r}}\right)}{n^{1/2}}.$$

In the notation of Theorem 56, if $b_n = n^{1/2}$, then b_n is positive, monotonic strictly increasing and tends to infinity as n tends to infinity. Also as $n \to \infty$,

$$\frac{a_{n+1} - a_n}{b_{n+1} - b_n} = \frac{\sinh \dfrac{\theta}{\sqrt{(n+1)}}}{\sqrt{(n+1)} - \sqrt{n}}$$

$$= \left\{ \frac{\sinh \dfrac{\theta}{\sqrt{(n+1)}}}{\dfrac{\theta}{\sqrt{(n+1)}}} \right\} \theta \frac{1}{\sqrt{(n+1)}[\sqrt{(n+1)} - \sqrt{n}]}$$

$$= \left\{ \frac{\sinh \dfrac{\theta}{\sqrt{(n+1)}}}{\dfrac{\theta}{\sqrt{(n+1)}}} \right\} \theta \left\{ \frac{\sqrt{(n+1)} + \sqrt{n}}{\sqrt{(n+1)}} \right\}$$

$$\to 2\theta.$$

Examples VII

(1) Evaluate the following limits:

(i) $\lim_{x \to 0} (e^{5x} - 2x)^{1/x}$;

(ii) $\lim_{x \to 0} \dfrac{2 \sinh x - \tanh x}{e^x - 1}$;

(iii) $\lim_{x \to 0} \dfrac{2 \log(1+x) + x^2 - 2x}{x^3}$;

(iv) $\lim_{x \to \infty} \left(\cosh \dfrac{2}{x} \right)^{x^2}$;

(v) $\lim_{x \to 0} \dfrac{x \cosh x - \sinh x}{\sinh 2x - 2 \sinh x}$;

(vi) $\lim_{x \to 0} \dfrac{x \tanh x}{\sqrt{(1 - x^2)} - 1}$;

H

(vii) $\lim_{x \to 1} (1 + 2 \log x)^{1/(x-1)}$; (viii) $\lim_{x \to 0} \dfrac{e^x - \log(1+x) - 1}{x^2(x+2)}$;

(ix) $\lim_{x \to 0} (1 + \sinh^2 x)^{2/x^2}$; (x) $\lim_{x \to \infty} \dfrac{\log \log x}{(\log x)^2}$;

(xi) $\lim_{x \to 0} \dfrac{(\sinh 2x)^3}{x[\log(1+x)]^2}$;

(xii) $\lim_{x \to \infty} x^{\alpha+1} \left(\sinh \dfrac{2}{x}\right)^\alpha \{\log(x+1) - \log x\}$.

(2) Evaluate the following limits as $n \to \infty$:

(i) $\lim \dfrac{1}{\sqrt{n}} \sum_{r=1}^{n} \log\left(1 + \dfrac{1}{\sqrt{r}}\right)$;

(ii) $\lim \dfrac{\log n}{n} \sum_{r=2}^{n} \sinh\left(\dfrac{\theta}{\log r}\right)$;

(iii) $\lim \dfrac{1}{(\log n)^2} \left\{-n + \sum_{v=1}^{n} \sqrt[v]{v}\right\}$;

(iv) $\lim \sqrt[n]{\left\{\cosh \theta \cosh \dfrac{\theta}{2} \dots \cosh \dfrac{\theta}{n}\right\}}$.

CHAPTER VIII

UPPER AND LOWER LIMITS

8.1. Definitions of upper and lower limits. Suppose that a function $f(x)$ is defined for all values of $x \geq A$, and suppose also that $f(x)$ is bounded above for $x \geq A$. Then

$$M(X) = \overline{\mathrm{Bd}}_{x \geq X} f(x)$$

is defined for all values of $X \geq A$. It is clear that $M(X)$ is a monotonic decreasing function of X, since, if $X_1 < X_2$, the set of numbers $f(x)$ for which $x \geq X_2$ is contained in the set of numbers $f(x)$ for which $x \geq X_1$. Hence

$$M(X_1) \geq M(X_2).$$

It follows from Theorem 33 that, as $X \to \infty$, $M(X)$ tends to a limit, and we define the symbol $\varlimsup_{x \to \infty} f(x)$ to be $\lim_{X \to \infty} M(X)$. If $f(x)$ is bounded above for $x \geq A$, $\varlimsup_{x \to \infty} f(x)$ is either some number l or is $-\infty$. If no number A can be found such that $f(x)$ is bounded above for $x \geq A$, the function $M(X)$ is undefined and, in these circumstances, we write

$$\varlimsup_{x \to \infty} f(x) = \infty.$$

Now suppose that $f(x)$ is bounded below for $x \geq A$. Then

$$m(X) = \underline{\mathrm{Bd}}_{x \geq X} f(x)$$

is defined for $X \geq A$, and it is easy to see that $m(X)$ is a monotonic increasing function of X, and therefore tends to a limit as $X \to \infty$. This limit defines the symbol $\varliminf_{x \to \infty} f(x)$. If $f(x)$ is bounded below for $x \geq A$, this limit is either a number l or $+\infty$. If no number A can be found such that $f(x)$ is bounded below for $x \geq A$, the function $m(X)$ is undefined and we write

$$\varliminf_{x \to \infty} f(x) = -\infty.$$

The value of $\varlimsup_{x \to \infty} f(x)$ is called the upper limit of $f(x)$ as $x \to \infty$, and that of $\varliminf_{x \to \infty} f(x)$, the lower limit of $f(x)$ as $x \to \infty$. From the definitions given above it is apparent that, for any function $f(x)$ defined for some range $x \geq A$, $\varlimsup_{x \to \infty} f(x)$ and $\varliminf_{x \to \infty} f(x)$ always exist, although they may be $\pm \infty$.

In the case of a bounded function $f(x)$ in the range $x \geq A$, it is clear that, for all $X \geq A$,

$$m(X) \leq M(X),$$

whence

$$\lim_{X \to \infty} m(X) \leq \lim_{X \to \infty} M(X),$$

and this is the same as saying that

$$\varliminf_{x \to \infty} f(x) \leq \varlimsup_{x \to \infty} f(x).$$

The same relation also holds in the case when $f(x)$ is not bounded, if we interpret $-\infty$ as being less than any number l and $+\infty$ as being greater than any number l.

In the same way, we may define what we mean by $\varlimsup_{n \to \infty} f(n)$, $\varliminf_{n \to \infty} f(n)$ in the case of a function $f(n)$, defined for positive integral values of $n \geq A$. The following examples illustrate the meaning of the definitions.

Example. Determine $\varlimsup f(n)$, $\varliminf f(n)$, where

(i) $f(n) = \dfrac{(-1)^n n}{2n+1}$,   (ii) $f(n) = \dfrac{(-1)^n (n+1)}{2n+1}$.

In (i) we have

$$|f(n)| = \frac{n}{2n+1} = \tfrac{1}{2}\left\{1 - \frac{1}{2n+1}\right\},$$

which shows that $|f(n)|$ is monotonic increasing. Further, as n increases through the even integers, $f(n)$ increases and tends to $\tfrac{1}{2}$ as $n \to \infty$; and, as n increases through the odd integers, $f(n)$ diminishes and tends to $-\tfrac{1}{2}$ as $n \to \infty$. Thus

$$M(N) = \underset{n \geq N}{\mathrm{Bd}}\, f(n) = \tfrac{1}{2}, \quad m(N) = \underset{n \geq N}{\underline{\mathrm{Bd}}}\, f(n) = -\tfrac{1}{2},$$

and these hold for any positive integer N. Hence

$$\overline{\lim_{n \to \infty}}\, f(n) = \lim_{N \to \infty} M(N) = \tfrac{1}{2},$$

$$\underline{\lim_{n \to \infty}}\, f(n) = \lim_{N \to \infty} m(N) = -\tfrac{1}{2}.$$

In (ii) we have

$$|f(n)| = \frac{n+1}{2n+1} = \tfrac{1}{2}\left\{1 + \frac{1}{2n+1}\right\},$$

which shows that $|f(n)|$ is monotonic decreasing. Further, as n increases through the even integers, $f(n)$ diminishes and tends to $\tfrac{1}{2}$ as $n \to \infty$, and, as n increases through the odd integers, $f(n)$ increases and tends to $-\tfrac{1}{2}$ as $n \to \infty$. Hence, when N is even,

$$M(N) = \underset{n \geq N}{\overline{\mathrm{Bd}}}\, f(n) = \frac{N+1}{2N+1}, \; m(N) = \underset{n \geq N}{\underline{\mathrm{Bd}}}\, f(n) = -\frac{(N+2)}{2N+3},$$

and, when N is odd,

$$M(N) = \frac{N+2}{2N+3}, \quad m(N) = -\frac{(N+1)}{2N+1}.$$

It follows that

$$\overline{\lim_{n \to \infty}}\, f(n) = \lim_{N \to \infty} M(N) = \tfrac{1}{2},$$

$$\underline{\lim_{n \to \infty}}\, f(n) = \lim_{N \to \infty} m(N) = -\tfrac{1}{2}.$$

We now derive an alternative definition for upper and lower limits.

THEOREM 57. *If* $\overline{\lim\limits_{x \to \infty}} f(x) = l$ *then, given any positive number* ε, (i) *we can find a positive number* X_1 *such that* $f(x) < l + \varepsilon$, *for all* $x > X_1$, *and* (ii), *if we choose any positive number* X_2, *there are values of* $x \geqq X_2$ *for which* $f(x) > l - \varepsilon$. *Conversely, if* (i) *and* (ii) *are satisfied, then* $\overline{\lim\limits_{x \to \infty}} f(x) = l$.

Suppose that $\overline{\lim\limits_{x \to \infty}} f(x) = l$. Then there is a number A, such that $f(x)$ is bounded above for $x \geqq A$, and

$$\lim_{X \to \infty} M(X) = \lim_{X \to \infty} \overline{\mathrm{Bd}}_{x \geqq X} f(x) = l.$$

Hence, given ε, we can find X_1 such that

$$l - \tfrac{1}{2}\varepsilon < M(X) < l + \tfrac{1}{2}\varepsilon,$$

for all values of $X \geqq X_1$. By the definition of $M(X)$, we have $f(x) \leqq M(X_1)$ for all values of $x > X_1$, whence, for such x,

$$f(x) \leqq M(X_1) < l + \tfrac{1}{2}\varepsilon < l + \varepsilon,$$

which proves (i).

Now choose any positive number X_2. If $X_2 > X_1$, we have $M(X_2) > l - \tfrac{1}{2}\varepsilon$. If $X_2 \leqq X_1$, we have

$$M(X_2) \geqq M(X_1) \geqq M(X)$$

for all $X > X_1$, and this in turn is greater than $l - \tfrac{1}{2}\varepsilon$. Hence, for any number X_2, $M(X_2) > l - \tfrac{1}{2}\varepsilon$. By the definition of $M(X_2)$, there is a number $x \geqq X_2$, such that $f(x) > M(X_2) - \tfrac{1}{2}\varepsilon$. For such a number x, we have $f(x) > M(X_2) - \tfrac{1}{2}\varepsilon > l - \varepsilon$, which proves (ii).

Conversely, suppose that (i) and (ii) are satisfied. From (i) and the definition of $M(X)$, we have,† for any $X > X_1$, $M(X) \leqq l + \varepsilon$. Choose any value $X > X_1$. Then, from (ii),

---

† We are using here the fact that if $f(x) < B$ then $\overline{\mathrm{Bd}}\, f(x) \leqq B$. This may be proved immediately by deriving a contradiction from the assumption that $\overline{\mathrm{Bd}}\, f(x) > B$.

there is a number $x > X > X_1$, such that $f(x) > l - \varepsilon$. Hence $M(X) > l - \varepsilon$ for every $X > X_1$. Thus, for such X,

$$| M(X) - l | \leqq \varepsilon,$$

so that $M(X) \to l$ as $X \to \infty$. The converse follows.

THEOREM 58. *If* $\overline{\lim\limits_{x \to \infty}} f(x) = l$, *then* $\underline{\lim\limits_{x \to \infty}} \{-f(x)\} = -l$, *and conversely.*

If $\overline{\lim\limits_{x \to \infty}} f(x) = l$, then $M(X) = \overline{\text{Bd}}_{x \geqq X} f(x) \to l$ as $X \to \infty$. But $\overline{\text{Bd}}_{x \geqq X} f(x) = -\underline{\text{Bd}}_{x \geqq X} \{-f(x)\}$, by Theorem 1. Using dashed symbols when referring to the function $-f(x)$, this gives $m'(X) = -M(X) \to -l$, as $X \to \infty$. The converse follows at once from the same relation.

The next theorem provides us with an alternative definition for the statement $\underline{\lim\limits_{x \to \infty}} f(x) = l$, and follows at once from Theorems 57 and 58 by considering the function $-f(x)$.

THEOREM 59. *If* $\underline{\lim\limits_{x \to \infty}} f(x) = l$, *then, given any positive* ε, (i) *we can find a positive number* X_1, *such that* $f(x) > l - \varepsilon$ *for all* $x > X_1$, *and* (ii), *if we choose any positive number* X_2, *there are values of* $x \geqq X_2$ *for which* $f(x) < l + \varepsilon$. *Conversely, if* (i) *and* (ii) *are satisfied, then* $\underline{\lim\limits_{x \to \infty}} f(x) = l$.

Just as in the case of ordinary limits, it is easy to frame definitions for the symbols

$$\overline{\lim\limits_{x \to -\infty}} f(x), \quad \underline{\lim\limits_{x \to -\infty}} f(x).$$

These are, respectively,

$$\overline{\lim\limits_{y \to \infty}} f(-y), \quad \underline{\lim\limits_{y \to \infty}} f(-y).$$

Suppose now that $f(x)$ is defined in an interval surrounding the point a, except possibly at a itself, and suppose that $f(x)$ is bounded in this interval. Let

$$M(\delta) = \overline{\text{Bd}}\, f(x), \quad 0 < | x - a | \leqq \delta,$$

where it is supposed that the interval $|x-a| \leqq \delta$, is contained in the given interval. Then, as δ diminishes, $M(\delta)$ does not increase, and therefore has a limit when $\delta \to 0$. This limit is called the upper limit of $f(x)$ when $x \to a$ and is written $\varlimsup_{x \to a} f(x)$. If $f(x)$ is not bounded above in any interval containing a we write $\varlimsup_{x \to a} f(x) = \infty$. If we consider, not all values of $f(x)$ in $|x-a| \leqq \delta$, but only those for which $a < x \leqq a+\delta$, and calculate the least upper bound of $f(x)$ for such values of x, the value of the limit of this least upper bound when $\delta \to 0$ is called the upper limit of $f(x)$, when x tends to a from the right, and is denoted by $\varlimsup_{x \to a+} f(x)$. Similarly, by considering only values of $f(x)$ for which $a-\delta \leqq x < a$, we obtain the upper limit of $f(x)$ as x tends to a from the left, and this is denoted by $\varlimsup_{x \to a-} f(x)$.

The usual convention applies, in regard to these upper limits, when $f(x)$ is not bounded above in any interval with a as left hand or right hand end-point.

Lower limits corresponding to these three cases are defined in a similar way, with greatest lower bounds substituted for least upper bounds in each case.

By making the substitutions

$$x = a + \frac{1}{y}, \quad Y = \frac{1}{\delta},$$

it is clear that

$$\varlimsup_{x \to a+} f(x) = \lim_{\delta \to 0} \left\{ \underset{a < x \leqq a+\delta}{\overline{\mathrm{Bd}}}\, f(x) \right\} = \lim_{\delta \to 0} \left\{ \underset{y \geqq 1/\delta}{\overline{\mathrm{Bd}}}\, f\left(a + \frac{1}{y}\right) \right\}$$

$$= \lim_{Y \to \infty} \left\{ \underset{y \geqq Y}{\overline{\mathrm{Bd}}}\, f\left(a + \frac{1}{y}\right) \right\}$$

$$= \varlimsup_{y \to \infty} f\left(a + \frac{1}{y}\right),$$

and, by making the substitutions

$$x = a - \frac{1}{y}, \quad Y = \frac{1}{\delta},$$

that

$$\varlimsup_{x \to a-} f(x) = \varlimsup_{y \to \infty} f\left(a - \frac{1}{y}\right).$$

Similar relations clearly hold for lower limits.

Writing δ_1 for $1/X_1$ and δ_2 for $1/X_2$ in Theorem 57, we see that the statement $\varlimsup\limits_{x \to a+} f(x) = l$ is equivalent to the statement that, given any positive ε, (i) we can find a positive number δ_1, such that $f(x) < l + \varepsilon$ for all values of x satisfying $0 < x - a < \delta_1$, and (ii), if we choose any positive number δ_2, there are values of x satisfying $0 < x - a \leqq \delta_2$ for which $f(x) > l - \varepsilon$. Similarly, to say that $\varlimsup\limits_{x \to a-} f(x) = l$ is to say (i) and (ii) above, but with $a - x$ replacing $x - a$ throughout. Analogous alternative statements for lower limits when $x \to a+$ or $x \to a-$ follow from Theorem 59.

THEOREM 60. *We have*

$$\varlimsup_{x \to a} f(x) = \text{Max}\left\{ \varlimsup_{x \to a+} f(x), \ \varlimsup_{x \to a-} f(x) \right\},$$

where $\text{Max}(z_1, z_2)$ *means the larger of* z_1 *and* z_2, *if these are unequal, and means either* z_1 *or* z_2, *if these are equal.*

We shall suppose that there is an interval surrounding the point a within which $f(x)$ is bounded above. If this is not the case, $\varlimsup\limits_{x \to a} f(x) = +\infty$ and one, at least, of the upper limits on the right is also $+\infty$.

Let δ be such that the interval $|x - a| \leqq \delta$ lies in the above interval, and let

$$M(\delta) = \underset{0 < |x-a| \leqq \delta}{\overline{\text{Bd}}}\ f(x), \quad M_1(\delta) = \underset{a < x \leqq a + \delta}{\overline{\text{Bd}}}\ f(x),$$
$$M_2(\delta) = \underset{a - \delta \leqq x < a}{\overline{\text{Bd}}}\ f(x).$$

Then $M(\delta)$ is the larger of $M_1(\delta)$ and $M_2(\delta)$ and, for all suitably small positive δ, we have

$$M_1(\delta) \leqq M(\delta), \quad M_2(\delta) \leqq M(\delta),$$

whence

$$\varlimsup_{x \to a+} f(x) \leqq \varlimsup_{x \to a} f(x), \quad \varlimsup_{x \to a-} f(x) \leqq \varlimsup_{x \to a} f(x),$$

so that

$$\varlimsup_{x \to a} f(x) \geqq \operatorname{Max} \left\{ \varlimsup_{x \to a+} f(x), \; \varlimsup_{x \to a-} f(x) \right\}.$$

The inequality cannot hold, for, suppose the left hand side is l and the right hand side l_1, with $l > l_1$, and suppose also that l_1 is, for example, $\varlimsup_{x \to a+} f(x)$. Then there is a positive number δ_1, such that, for all values of δ in $0 < \delta \leqq \delta_1$, $M_2(\delta) \leqq M_1(\delta)$. Suppose ε is any positive number less than $\frac{1}{2}(l - l_1)$. Then there is a positive number δ_2, such that $M(\delta) > l - \varepsilon = \frac{1}{2}(l + l_1)$ whenever $0 < \delta \leqq \delta_2$, and a positive number δ_3, such that $M_1(\delta) < l_1 + \varepsilon = \frac{1}{2}(l + l_1)$ whenever $0 < \delta \leqq \delta_3$. Thus, for any δ smaller than the least of δ_1, δ_2, δ_3, we have $M(\delta)$ greater than both $M_1(\delta)$ and $M_2(\delta)$, and this is not possible.

This argument does not apply to the case when the upper limits on the right are both $-\infty$, but it can be easily adapted to show that the left hand side is then also $-\infty$.

Example. If $f(x)$
$$\begin{cases} = 1, \text{ when } x \text{ is any positive irrational} \\ \quad \text{number,} \\ = \tfrac{1}{2}, \text{ when } x \text{ is any negative irrational} \\ \quad \text{number,} \\ = 0, \text{ when } x \text{ is any rational number} \\ \quad \text{other than zero,} \end{cases}$$

then

$$\varlimsup_{x \to 0} f(x) = 1, \quad \varlimsup_{x \to 0+} f(x) = 1, \quad \varlimsup_{x \to 0-} f(x) = \tfrac{1}{2},$$

$$\varliminf_{x \to 0} f(x) = \varliminf_{x \to 0-} f(x) = \varliminf_{x \to 0+} f(x) = 0.$$

These relations follow at once since, in the notation of Theorem 60, for any positive δ,

$$M(\delta) = 1, \quad M_1(\delta) = 1, \quad M_2(\delta) = \tfrac{1}{2},$$

$$m(\delta) = m_1(\delta) = m_2(\delta) = 0.$$

8.2. Some properties of upper and lower limits. We have already seen that $\overline{\lim}\, f(x) = -\underline{\lim}_{x\to\infty}\{-f(x)\}$. The proof of this theorem applies with minor modifications to the cases when $x\to-\infty$, $x\to a+$, $x\to a-$, or $x\to a$. The theorems below will all be proved for the case $x\to a$, but similar proofs apply to the other cases. Since we shall be dealing throughout with upper and lower limits as $x\to a$, we shall omit $x\to a$ from the symbols $\overline{\lim}_{x\to a} f(x)$, $\underline{\lim}_{x\to a} f(x)$ and write simply $\overline{\lim}\, f(x)$, $\underline{\lim}\, f(x)$. Another advantage of using this notation is that, in the enunciation of each theorem, x may, by implication, tend to $+\infty$, to $-\infty$, to $a+$, to $a-$, or to a.

THEOREM 61. *If c is a positive constant, then*

(i) $\overline{\lim}\, cf(x) = c\, \overline{\lim}\, f(x)$,

(ii) $\underline{\lim}\, cf(x) = c\, \underline{\lim}\, f(x)$.

If $f(x)$ is not bounded above in some interval containing a, neither is $cf(x)$, and the result is true with the customary interpretation of infinity. If $f(x)$ is bounded above in some interval containing a, let

$$M(\delta) = \overline{\mathrm{Bd}}\, f(x), \quad M'(\delta) = \overline{\mathrm{Bd}}\, cf(x),$$

where the bounds refer to the interval $0 < |x-a| \leqq \delta$.

Then, by Theorem 2, since c is positive, $M'(\delta) = cM(\delta)$. Let $\delta\to 0$, and the result follows. A similar proof holds for lower limits.

THEOREM 62. *We have, when the right hand sides have meaning,*

(i) $\overline{\lim} \{f(x) + g(x)\} \leqq \overline{\lim} f(x) + \overline{\lim} g(x),$

(ii) $\underline{\lim} \{f(x) + g(x)\} \geqq \underline{\lim} f(x) + \underline{\lim} g(x).$

It will be sufficient to consider the cases when $f(x)$ and $g(x)$ are bounded in some interval containing a. Let

$$M_1(\delta) = \overline{\mathrm{Bd}} f(x), \quad M_2(\delta) = \overline{\mathrm{Bd}} g(x),$$

$$M(\delta) = \overline{\mathrm{Bd}} \{f(x) + g(x)\},$$

where the bounds refer to the interval $0 < |x - a| \leqq \delta$. Then, from Theorem 5, we have

$$M(\delta) \leqq M_1(\delta) + M_2(\delta).$$

Hence, using Theorem 12,

$$\begin{aligned}
\lim_{\delta \to 0} M(\delta) &\leqq \lim_{\delta \to 0} \{M_1(\delta) + M_2(\delta)\} \\
&= \lim_{\delta \to 0} M_1(\delta) + \lim_{\delta \to 0} M_2(\delta) \\
&= \overline{\lim} f(x) + \overline{\lim} g(x).
\end{aligned}$$

The second relation follows from the first by considering $-f(x)$ and $-g(x)$.

THEOREM 63. *We have, when the right hand sides have meaning,*

(i) $\overline{\lim} \{f(x) - g(x)\} \leqq \overline{\lim} f(x) - \underline{\lim} g(x),$

(ii) $\underline{\lim} \{f(x) - g(x)\} \geqq \underline{\lim} f(x) - \overline{\lim} g(x).$

The first relation follows since

$$\begin{aligned}
\overline{\lim} \{f(x) - g(x)\} &= \overline{\lim} [f(x) + \{-g(x)\}] \\
&\leqq \overline{\lim} f(x) + \overline{\lim} \{-g(x)\} \\
&= \overline{\lim} f(x) - \underline{\lim} g(x).
\end{aligned}$$

The second follows similarly.

THEOREM 64. *If, throughout an interval containing* a, $x \neq a$, $f(x) \leq g(x)$, *then*

$$\overline{\lim} f(x) \leq \overline{\lim} g(x)$$
$$\underline{\lim} f(x) \leq \underline{\lim} g(x).$$

It is sufficient to consider the cases when $f(x)$ and $g(x)$ are bounded in the interval. The reader may satisfy himself as to the truth of the relations in other cases.

If $M_1(\delta) = \overline{\mathrm{Bd}} f(x)$, $M_2(\delta) = \overline{\mathrm{Bd}} g(x)$, where the bounds refer to the interval $0 < |x-a| \leq \delta$, then $M_1(\delta) \leq M_2(\delta)$. Also, if $m_1(\delta)$, $m_2(\delta)$ denote the corresponding greatest lower bounds, we have $m_1(\delta) \leq m_2(\delta)$.

The results follow on letting $\delta \to 0$.

THEOREM 65. *If, for all values of* x *in an interval containing* a, $x \neq a$, *we have* $A \leq f(x) \leq B$, *then*

$$A \leq \underline{\lim} f(x) \leq \overline{\lim} f(x) \leq B.$$

This follows from the previous theorem, since $\overline{\lim} A = \underline{\lim} A = A$ and $\overline{\lim} B = \underline{\lim} B = B$.

We have seen in Chapter 3 that a function, even if defined for suitable values of x, need not tend to a limit, and we have also seen that a function always possesses an upper and a lower limit. The following theorem gives a criterion for the existence of a limit.

THEOREM 66. *A necessary and sufficient condition that* $f(x)$ *should tend to a limit as* $x \to a$ *is that*

$$\overline{\lim_{x \to a}} f(x) = \underline{\lim_{x \to a}} f(x).$$

When $\overline{\lim} f(x)$ *and* $\underline{\lim} f(x)$ *are both* $+\infty$ *or are both* $-\infty$, *the result is to be interpreted to mean that* $\lim f(x)$ *is* $+\infty$ *or* $-\infty$ *respectively.*

We deal with necessity first. Suppose that $\lim_{x \to a} f(x) = l$. Then, given any positive ε, we can find a positive number δ such that, for all values of x satisfying $0 < |x-a| < \delta$, we have

$$l - \varepsilon < f(x) < l + \varepsilon.$$

Hence, by Theorems 57 and 58, $\overline{\lim} f(x) = \underline{\lim} f(x) = l$.

If $\lim\limits_{x \to a} f(x) = \infty$, given any positive number K, we can find a positive number δ such that, whenever $0 < |x-a| < \delta$, we have $f(x) > K$. Hence $\underline{\lim} f(x) = +\infty$ and, *a fortiori*, $\overline{\lim} f(x) = +\infty$.

A similar argument deals with the case when $f(x) \to -\infty$ as $x \to \infty$. The condition is therefore necessary.

To prove sufficiency, assume first that

$$\overline{\lim} f(x) = \underline{\lim} f(x) = l.$$

Then, from Theorems 57 and 59, given any positive ε, we can find δ_1 such that $f(x) < l+\varepsilon$ whenever $0 < |x-a| < \delta_1$, and δ_2 such that $f(x) > l-\varepsilon$ whenever $0 < |x-a| < \delta_2$. If $\delta = \min(\delta_1, \delta_2)$, we then have $l-\varepsilon < f(x) < l+\varepsilon$ for $0 < |x-a| < \delta$. Hence $f(x) \to l$ as $x \to a$.

If $\overline{\lim} f(x) = \underline{\lim} f(x) = \infty$, then, given any positive number K, we can find δ_1 such that $f(x) > K$ whenever $0 < |x-a| < \delta_1$. Hence $f(x) \to \infty$ as $x \to a$. Similarly, when $\overline{\lim} f(x)$ and $\underline{\lim} f(x)$ are both $-\infty$.

Another necessary and sufficient condition, this time that $f(x)$ should tend to a finite limit, is provided by the following theorem.

THEOREM 67.   *A necessary and sufficient condition that, as x tends to a, f(x) should tend to a finite limit is that, given any positive number ε, we can find another positive number δ, such that, if x_1 and x_2 are any two points other than a in the interval $|x-a| < \delta$, we have $|f(x_1) - f(x_2)| < \varepsilon$.*

Suppose first that $f(x)$ tends to a limit l as $x \to a$. Then, given any positive number ε, we can find a positive number δ such that

$$|f(x) - l| < \tfrac{1}{2}\varepsilon,$$

whenever $0 < |x-a| < \delta$. Suppose that x_1, x_2 are any two points other than a in the interval $(a-\delta, a+\delta)$. Then

$$|f(x_1) - l| < \tfrac{1}{2}\varepsilon, \quad |f(x_2) - l| < \tfrac{1}{2}\varepsilon,$$

and therefore

$$|f(x_1)-f(x_2)| = |\{f(x_1)-l\}+\{l-f(x_2)\}|$$
$$\leq |f(x_1)-l| + |f(x_2)-l|$$
$$< \tfrac{1}{2}\varepsilon+\tfrac{1}{2}\varepsilon = \varepsilon.$$

Hence the condition is necessary.

Suppose now that the condition is satisfied. Then, for any pair of points x_1, x_2 other than a in the interval $(a-\delta,\ a+\delta)$, we have $|f(x_1)-f(x_2)| < \varepsilon$, and this is the same as

$$f(x_2)-\varepsilon < f(x_1) < f(x_2)+\varepsilon.$$

Keep x_2 fixed in the interval $(a-\delta,\ a+\delta)$ and let x_1 tend to a. Then from Theorem 65

$$f(x_2)-\varepsilon \leq \varliminf_{x_1\to a} f(x_1) \leq \varlimsup_{x_1\to a} f(x_1) \leq f(x_2)+\varepsilon,$$

whence

$$0 \leq \varlimsup_{x\to a} f(x) - \varliminf_{x\to a} f(x) \leq 2\varepsilon.$$

But ε may be as small as we please. Hence

$$\varlimsup_{x\to a} f(x) = \varliminf_{x\to a} f(x),$$

and these are both finite, since they are greater than or equal to $f(x_2)-\varepsilon$ and less than or equal to $f(x_2)+\varepsilon$. Thus $f(x)$ tends to a finite limit as $x\to a$. Hence sufficiency is established.

There is, of course, a corresponding theorem for the case when $x\to\infty$, and it is worth stating it in detail.

THEOREM 68. *A necessary and sufficient condition that, as x tends to infinity, $f(x)$ should tend to a finite limit, is that, given any positive number ε, we can find a positive number X such that, for any two numbers x_1, x_2 satisfying $x_1 > X$, $x_2 > X$, we have $|f(x_1)-f(x_2)| < \varepsilon$.*

Adapting this to the case of the positive integral variable we have the following theorem:—

THEOREM 69. *A necessary and sufficient condition that, as n tends to infinity, f(n) should tend to a finite limit, is that, given any positive number ε, we can find a positive integer N such that, for all values of n > N and any positive integral value of p,* $|f(n+p)-f(n)| < \varepsilon$

The substitution of N for the more usual X here presents no difficulty since, if a property is true for all positive integral values of n greater than some number X, it is also true *a fortiori* for all positive integral values of n greater than the positive integer next greater than X. A strict conclusion from Theorem 68 would be that, for any positive integers n_1, n_2 greater than N, we have

$$|f(n_2)-f(n_1)| < \varepsilon.$$

In Theorem 69 we have replaced n_1 by some integer n greater than N, and n_2 by $n+p$, which is of course also greater than N.

It should also be observed that the necessary and sufficient condition in Theorem 69 may also be expressed by saying that, for any positive integer p, $f(n+p)-f(n)\to0$ as $n\to\infty$.

The last three theorems are regarded as different instances of what is called the **general principle of convergence**.

Theorem 69 also provides us with a necessary and sufficient condition for the convergence of a series $\sum\limits_{n=1}^{\infty} a_n$, if we replace $f(n)$ by A_n where $A_n = a_1+a_2+\ldots+a_n$. The condition $|f(n+p)-f(n)| < \varepsilon$ then takes the form $|A_{n+p}-A_n| < \varepsilon$, and this is the same as $\left|\sum\limits_{v=n+1}^{n+p} a_v\right| < \varepsilon$.

Thus, a necessary and sufficient condition that the series

$$\sum_{n=1}^{\infty} a_n$$

be convergent is that, given any positive ε, we can find a positive integer N such that

$$\left| \sum_{v=n+1}^{n+p} a_v \right| < \varepsilon,$$

whenever $n > N$ and for any positive integer p.

Examples VIII

(1) Evaluate the following upper and lower limits:—

    (i) $\varlimsup_{n \to \infty} (-1)^n \tanh n$;   (ii) $\varliminf_{n \to \infty} (-1)^n \tanh n$;

    (iii) $\varlimsup_{n \to \infty} \left(n \sinh \dfrac{1}{n} + (-1)^n \tanh n \right)$;

    (iv) $\varliminf_{n \to \infty} \left(n \sinh \dfrac{1}{n} + (-1)^n \tanh n \right)$.

(2) If $f(n)$ is defined as follows:—

$$f(n) \begin{cases} = 2, \text{ when } n \text{ is a multiple of 4}; \\ = 0, \text{ when } n \text{ is even but not a multiple of 4}; \\ = 1, \text{ when } n \text{ is odd}, \end{cases}$$

determine $\varlimsup_{n \to \infty} f(n)$ and $\varliminf_{n \to \infty} f(n)$.

(3) If $f(x) = x$, when x is rational,

           $= 1$, when x is irrational,

evaluate $\varlimsup_{x \to 0} f(x)$, $\varliminf_{x \to 0} f(x)$.

I

(4) Prove that the series

$$\sum_{n=2}^{\infty} (\log n)^{-\alpha}$$

is not convergent for any value of α, and that the series

$$\sum_{n=1}^{\infty} n^{-\alpha}$$

is not convergent for $\alpha \leqq 1$.

CHAPTER IX

THE CIRCULAR FUNCTIONS

9.1. Definitions of sin x, cos x. In Chapter 6 we defined and obtained properties of the hyperbolic functions sinh x, cosh x, tanh x, and it would be unnatural to leave the elementary course on analysis, which is the subject matter of this book, without considering the well-known circular functions sin x, cos x and tan x.

Let

$$C_n(x) = 1 - \frac{x^2}{2!} + \frac{x^4}{4!} - \ldots + (-1)^{n-1} \frac{x^{2n-2}}{(2n-2)!},$$

$$S_n(x) = x - \frac{x^3}{3!} + \ldots + (-1)^{n-1} \frac{x^{2n-1}}{(2n-1)!},$$

which define $C_n(x)$ and $S_n(x)$ for all values of x and for all positive integral values of n. Let p be any positive integer and x any real number. Then, for $n > \frac{1}{2}|x|$,

$$
\begin{aligned}
|C_{n+p}(x) - C_n(x)| &\leqq \frac{|x|^{2n}}{(2n)!} + \frac{|x|^{2n+2}}{(2n+2)!} + \ldots + \frac{|x|^{2n+2p-2}}{(2n+2p-2)!} \\
&< \frac{|x|^{2n}}{(2n)!} \left\{ 1 + \frac{|x|^2}{(2n)^2} + \ldots + \frac{|x|^{2p-2}}{(2n)^{2p-2}} \right\} \\
&< \frac{|x|^{2n}}{(2n)!} \frac{1}{1 - \left(\dfrac{x}{2n}\right)^2},
\end{aligned}
$$

by the inequality in 5.2. The last expression tends to zero as $n \to \infty$ for every fixed x, by the argument in Theorem 52.

It follows from Theorem 69 that $C_n(x)$ tends to a non-infinite limit as $n \to \infty$, for every real number x. This limit is denoted by $\cos x$. In the language of infinite series

$$\cos x = 1 - \frac{x^2}{2!} + \frac{x^4}{4!} - ...,$$

the series being convergent for every value of x. In the same way, it is easy to show that $S_{n+p}(x) - S_n(x)$ tends to zero as $n \to \infty$ for every value of x. The limit of $S_n(x)$ as $n \to \infty$ is denoted by $\sin x$, and we have

$$\sin x = x - \frac{x^3}{3!} + \frac{x^5}{5!} - ...,$$

the series being convergent for all values of x.

THEOREM 70. *The functions* $\sin x$ *and* $\cos x$ *are differentiable for all values of* x *and, at the point* x,

$$D \sin x = \cos x, \quad D \cos x = - \sin x.$$

Let x be any real number and h such that $|h| < 1$. Then

$$\frac{\sin(x+h) - \sin x}{h} = \lim_{n \to \infty} \frac{S_n(x+h) - S_n(x)}{h}.$$

Now $S_n(x)$ is differentiable as many times as we please for all x, whence, by Taylor's Theorem,

$$\frac{S_n(x+h) - S_n(x)}{h} = S_n'(x) + \frac{h}{2!} S_n''(x + \theta h)$$

$$= C_n(x) + \frac{h}{2!} S_n''(x + \theta h).$$

When n tends to infinity, the left hand side has a limit and so also has $C_n(x)$. Hence $S_n''(x + \theta h)$ tends to a finite limit, by Theorem 12. Now

$$\left| S_n''(x+\theta h) \right|$$

$$= \left| -(x+\theta h) + \frac{(x+\theta h)^3}{3!} + \ldots + (-1)^{n-1}\frac{(x+\theta h)^{2n-3}}{(2n-3)!} \right|$$

$$\leq \left\{ |x+\theta h| + \frac{|x+\theta h|^3}{3!} + \ldots + \frac{|x+\theta h|^{2n-3}}{(2n-3)!} \right\}$$

$$\leq \sinh\left(|x+\theta h|\right) \leq \sinh\left(|x|+1\right),$$

since $\sinh x$ is monotonic increasing for positive x, and $0 < \theta < 1$. Hence, as $n \to \infty$, $\lim S_n''(x+\theta h)$ lies between $-\sinh\left(|x|+1\right)$ and $+\sinh\left(|x|+1\right)$. Denote this limit by $L(x, h)$. Then

$$\left| \frac{\sin(x+h)-\sin x}{h} - \cos x \right| = \left| \frac{h}{2} L(x, h) \right| \to 0$$

as $h \to 0$ for every fixed x. The first result is therefore established, and the second may be dealt with similarly.

Since, for every positive integer n, $C_n(0) = 1$ and $S_n(0) = 0$, it follows that $\sin 0 = 0$ and $\cos 0 = 1$. Also, from Theorem 70, $\sin x$ is differentiable at $x = 0$, whence

$$\lim_{h \to 0} \frac{\sin h}{h} = 1.$$

Since $\sin x$ and $\cos x$ are differentiable for all x, it follows that $\sin x$ and $\cos x$ are continuous for all x. Moreover, $\sin x$ and $\cos x$ are differentiable as many times as we please for all x, and

$$D^{2n}\sin x = (-1)^n\sin x, \quad D^{2n-1}\sin x = (-1)^{n-1}\cos x,$$

$$D^{2n}\cos x = (-1)^n\cos x, \quad D^{2n-1}\cos x = (-1)^n\sin x,$$

where D^{2n} denotes

$$\frac{d^{2n}}{dx^{2n}}.$$

From the definitions of $\sin x$ and $\cos x$ it is clear that

$$\sin(-x) = -\sin x,$$
$$\cos(-x) = \cos x.$$

9.2. The addition theorem for $\sin x$, $\cos x$. Since, for all values of x,

$$D^2 \sin x = -\sin x, \quad D^2 \cos x = -\cos x,$$

we see that the functions $y = \sin x$, $y = \cos x$ satisfy the differential equation

$$\frac{d^2 y}{dx^2} + y = 0,$$

for all values of x. Let

$$y_1 = y_1(x) = \sin x, \; y_2 = y_2(x) = \cos x.$$

Then

$$y_1'' + y_1 = 0, \quad y_2'' + y_2 = 0,$$

whence $y_2 y_1'' - y_1 y_2'' = 0$, and this is the same as

$$\frac{d}{dx}(y_2 y_1' - y_1 y_2') = 0,$$

which relation holds for all values of x. Hence, by Theorem 48,

$$y_2 y_1' - y_1 y_2' = C,$$

where C is independent of x. For all values of x therefore

$$\cos^2 x + \sin^2 x = C,$$

and, in particular, this relation holds when $x = 0$, in which event $C = 1$. Thus, for all values of x,

$$\cos^2 x + \sin^2 x = 1.$$

From this relation it follows that, for all values of x,

$$-1 \leqq \cos x \leqq 1, \quad -1 \leqq \sin x \leqq 1.$$

Now suppose that $y_3 = y_3(x)$ is any other function which satisfies the differential equation for all values of x. Then

$$y_1'' + y_1 = 0, \quad y_3'' + y_3 = 0,$$

whence $y_3 y_1'' - y_1 y_3'' = 0$, and this is the same as

$$\frac{d}{dx}(y_3 y_1' - y_1 y_3') = 0,$$

which relation holds for all values of x. Hence, by Theorem 48,

$$y_3 y_1' - y_1 y_3' = A,$$

where A is independent of x. Similarly, by considering the relations

$$y_2'' + y_2 = 0, \quad y_3'' + y_3 = 0$$

we see that, for all values of x,

$$y_2 y_3' - y_3 y_2' = B,$$

where B is a constant independent of x. These relations may now be written

$$y_3 \cos x - y_3' \sin x = A,$$
$$y_3 \sin x + y_3' \cos x = B,$$

and the elimination of y_3' and the use of the relation

$$\cos^2 x + \sin^2 x = 1,$$

gives

$$y_3 = A \cos x + B \sin x.$$

It follows that any function which satisfies the differential equation for all values of x must be of the form $A \cos x + B \sin x$, where A and B are constants independent of x.

THEOREM 71. *If x and a are any real numbers,*

(i) $\sin(x+a) = \sin x \cos a + \cos x \sin a$
(ii) $\cos(x+a) = \cos x \cos a - \sin x \sin a$.

Regarding a as a fixed real number, we have, for all x,

$$D^2 \sin(x+a) = -\sin(x+a),$$

so that $\sin(x+a)$ satisfies the differential equation $y'' + y = 0$ for all values of x. Hence we may write

$$\sin(x+a) = A\cos x + B\sin x,$$

where A, B are independent of x. Differentiation of this relation gives

$$\cos(x+a) = -A\sin x + B\cos x.$$

These relations hold in particular when $x = 0$. Hence

$$A = \sin a, \quad B = \cos a,$$

and both results follow.

From these two formulæ many further well-known properties of the sine and cosine functions are immediately deducible. Thus

$$\sin 2a = 2\sin a\cos a,$$
$$\cos 2a = \cos^2 a - \sin^2 a,$$
$$\sin a + \sin b = 2\sin \tfrac{1}{2}(a+b)\cos \tfrac{1}{2}(a-b),$$
$$\cos a + \cos b = 2\cos \tfrac{1}{2}(a+b)\cos \tfrac{1}{2}(a-b).$$

9.3. The periodic property. Since $\cos 0 = 1$ and $\cos x$ is continuous for all values of x, there is an interval to the right of $x = 0$ within which $\cos x > 0$. That $\cos x < 0$ for some positive values of x is clear from the Taylor relation

$$\cos x = 1 - \frac{x^2}{2!} + \frac{x^4}{4!}\cos\theta x,$$

which, when $x = 2$, gives

$$\cos 2 = 1 - 2 + \tfrac{2}{3}\cos(2\theta)$$
$$= -1 + \tfrac{2}{3}\cos 2\theta$$
$$< 0,$$

since $\cos 2\theta$ does not exceed 1.

Let $(0, h)$ be any interval to the right of $x = 0$ within which $\cos x > 0$, and let $\frac{\pi}{2}$ denote the least upper bound of such values of h. Such a least upper bound does exist since $\cos x < 0$ for some positive values of x. It should be noted that this constitutes a *definition* of π. It is easy to see that $\cos \frac{\pi}{2} = 0$ for, if $\cos \frac{\pi}{2} > 0$, there is an interval to the right of $x = \frac{\pi}{2}$ within which $\cos x > 0$ and, if $\cos \frac{\pi}{2} < 0$, there is an interval to the left of $x = \frac{\pi}{2}$ within which $\cos x < 0$, and each of these statements is incompatible with the definition of $\frac{\pi}{2}$ as the least upper bound of values of h for which $\cos x > 0$ in $(0, h)$.

With this definition of $\frac{\pi}{2}$, we then have

$$\cos x > 0, \quad \left(0 \leqq x < \frac{\pi}{2}\right),$$

$$\cos \frac{\pi}{2} = 0.$$

Since $\sin^2 \frac{\pi}{2} = 1 - \cos^2 \frac{\pi}{2} = 1$, it follows that $\sin \frac{\pi}{2} = \pm 1$. The negative sign may be dispensed with, however, since, by Theorem 48, $\sin x$ is monotonic strictly increasing for $0 \leqq x < \frac{\pi}{2}$, and its value when $x = 0$ is zero. Since $D \cos x = -\sin x$ and $\sin x$ is positive for $0 < x \leqq \frac{\pi}{2}$ it follows, from Theorem 48, that $\cos x$ decreases strictly from 1 to 0 as x increases from 0 to $\frac{\pi}{2}$.

It will be noted that since $\cos 2 < 0$, π satisfies the relation $0 < \pi < 4$.

THEOREM 72. *For all values of* x,

(i) $\sin\left(x + \dfrac{\pi}{2}\right) = \cos x, \quad \cos\left(x + \dfrac{\pi}{2}\right) = -\sin x,$

(ii) $\sin(x+\pi) = -\sin x, \quad \cos(x+\pi) = -\cos x,$

(iii) $\sin(x+2\pi) = \sin x, \quad \cos(x+2\pi) = \cos x.$

(i) From Theorem 71, we have

$$\sin\left(x + \frac{\pi}{2}\right) = \sin x \cos \frac{\pi}{2} + \cos x \sin \frac{\pi}{2} = \cos x,$$

and the other result follows in the same way, or by differentiation. Putting $x = \dfrac{\pi}{2}$ in these results we see that $\sin \pi = 0$, $\cos \pi = -1$.

(ii) From Theorem 71,

$$\sin(x+\pi) = \sin x \cos \pi + \cos x \sin \pi = -\sin x,$$

and similarly for $\cos(x+\pi)$. In particular, putting $x = \pi$, $\sin 2\pi = 0$, $\cos 2\pi = 1$.

(iii) From Theorem 71,

$$\sin(x+2\pi) = \sin x \cos 2\pi + \cos x \sin 2\pi = \sin x,$$

and similarly for $\cos(x+2\pi)$.

Relations (i) show that, in $\left(\dfrac{\pi}{2}, \pi\right)$, the sine function runs through the same set of values as the cosine function in $\left(0, \dfrac{\pi}{2}\right)$; that is, it decreases strictly from 1 to 0. Also, in $\left(\dfrac{\pi}{2}, \pi\right)$, the cosine function runs through the same set of values as the sine function in $\left(0, \dfrac{\pi}{2}\right)$, but with the signs of these values reversed; that is, the cosine function decreases strictly from 0 to -1. Relations (ii) show that, in $(\pi, 2\pi)$, the sine function decreases from 0 to -1, which value is attained at the point $\dfrac{3\pi}{2}$, and then increases from -1 to 0, while the cosine function increases from -1 to $+1$, passing through the value zero at the point $\dfrac{3\pi}{2}$.

Relations (iii) show that, in $(2\pi, 4\pi)$, the sine and cosine functions run through the same set of values as in $(0, 2\pi)$. Indeed repetition of (iii) shows that, for any positive integer n,

$$\sin (x+2n\pi) = \sin x, \quad \cos (x+2n\pi) = \cos x,$$

and the same results are easily proved in the case when n is a negative integer. The values of $\sin x$ and $\cos x$ therefore recur at intervals of length 2π, and we say that $\sin x$ and $\cos x$ are periodic and have period 2π.

It also follows from the above discussion that $\sin x = 0$ at the points $x = m\pi$, where $m = 0, \pm 1, \pm 2, \ldots$, and at no other points, and that $\cos x = 0$ at the points $x = (m-\frac{1}{2})\pi$, where $m = 0, \pm 1, \pm 2, \ldots$, and at no other points. These points are called respectively the zeros of $\sin x$ and $\cos x$.

9.4. Other circular functions. For all values of x, except those mentioned, the functions $\tan x$, $\cot x$, $\sec x$, $\csc x$ are defined as follows :—

$$\tan x = \frac{\sin x}{\cos x}, \quad \{x \neq (m-\tfrac{1}{2})\pi\},$$

$$\cot x = \frac{\cos x}{\sin x}, \quad (x \neq m\pi),$$

$$\sec x = \frac{1}{\cos x}, \quad \{x \neq (m-\tfrac{1}{2})\pi\},$$

$$\csc x = \frac{1}{\sin x}, \quad (x \neq m\pi),$$

where m is any integer. Properties of $\sec x$, $\operatorname{cosec} x$ are obtainable at once from those of $\cos x$ and $\sin x$. For the function $\tan x$, we have

$$D \tan x = \sec^2 x, \quad \{x \neq (m-\tfrac{1}{2})\pi\},$$

so that $\tan x$ is monotonic strictly increasing in any interval throughout which it is defined. Also

$$\tan (x+a) = \frac{\sin (x+a)}{\cos (x+a)} = \frac{\sin x \cos a + \cos x \sin a}{\cos x \cos a - \sin x \sin a}$$

$$= \frac{\tan x + \tan a}{1 - \tan x \tan a},$$

for all values of x and a for which the functions concerned are defined. Since $\tan \pi = 0$ it follows that $\tan x$ is periodic and has period π. It is also clear that

$$\lim_{x \to \frac{\pi}{2}-} \tan x = +\infty, \quad \lim_{x \to \frac{\pi}{2}+} \tan x = -\infty,$$

and that the same results hold as x tends to any odd multiple of $\dfrac{\pi}{2}$.

Properties of $\cot x$ are at once obtainable from those of $\tan x$.

Examples IX

(1) Show that

$$\overline{\lim_{x \to 0+}} \left(x + \sin \frac{1}{x} \right) = 1, \quad \underline{\lim_{x \to 0+}} \left(x + \sin \frac{1}{x} \right) = -1.$$

(2) Show that

$$f(x) = x \sin \frac{1}{x}, \quad (x \neq 0),$$
$$= 0, \quad (x = 0),$$

is continuous but not differentiable at $x = 0$.

(3) Show that

$$f(x) = x^2 \sin \frac{1}{x}, \quad (x \neq 0),$$

$$= 0, \qquad (x = 0),$$

is differentiable at $x = 0$.

(4) Show that the relation

$$y = \tan x, \quad \left(-\frac{\pi}{2} < x < \frac{\pi}{2}\right),$$

defines x as a monotonic strictly increasing function of y for all values of y. Show, further, that x is a differentiable function of y for all values of y, and that

$$\frac{dx}{dy} = \frac{1}{1+y^2}.$$

[This function x of y is denoted by arc tan y or by $\tan^{-1} y$.]

(5) Show that the relation

$$y = \sin x, \quad \left(-\frac{\pi}{2} \leqq x \leqq \frac{\pi}{2}\right),$$

defines x as a monotonic function of y, which increases strictly from $-\frac{\pi}{2}$ to $+\frac{\pi}{2}$ as y increases from -1 to 1. Show also that x is a differentiable function of y for $-1 < y < 1$, and that

$$\frac{dx}{dy} = \frac{1}{\sqrt{(1-y^2)}}.$$

[This function x of y is denoted by arc sin y or by $\sin^{-1} y$.]

(6) By expanding arc sin y as far as the term in y^5, and putting $y = \frac{1}{2}$, obtain an approximation for π.

(7) Prove that, for all values of x,

$$e^x \sin x = \sum_{r=1}^{\infty} \frac{(x\sqrt{2})^r}{r!} \sin \frac{r\pi}{4}.$$

INDEX

135

REAL VARIABLE

PRINTED IN GREAT BRITAIN BY OLIVER AND BOYD LTD., EDINBURGH

Date